THE LIFE AND PERAMBULATIONS OF A MOUSE

Dorothy Kilner

The Life and Perambulations of a Mouse

Dorothy Kilner

© 1st World Library – Literary Society, 2005
PO Box 2211
Fairfield, IA 52556
www.1stworldlibrary.org
First Edition

LCCN: 2004091177

Softcover ISBN: 1-59540-623-9
Hardcover ISBN: 1-4218-0923-0
eBook ISBN: 1-59540-723-5

Purchase *"The Life and Perambulations of a Mouse"*
as a traditional bound book at:
www.1stWorldLibrary.org/purchase.asp?ISBN=1-59540-623-9

1st World Library Literary Society is a nonprofit
organization dedicated to promoting literacy by:

- Creating a free internet library accessible from any
  computer worldwide.
- Hosting writing competitions and offering book
  publishing scholarships.

**Readers interested in supporting literacy
through sponsorship, donations or
membership please contact:
literacy@1stworldlibrary.org
Check us out at: www.1stworldlibrary.ORG
and start downloading free ebooks today.**

The Life and Perambulations of a Mouse
contributed by the Mahaney Family
in support of
1st World Library Literary Society

INTRODUCTION

During a remarkably severe winter, when a prodigious fall of snow confined everybody to their habitations, who were happy enough to have one to shelter them from the inclemency of the season, and were hot obliged by business to expose themselves to its rigour, I was on a visit to Meadow Hall; where had assembled likewise a large party of young folk, who all seemed, by their harmony and good humour, to strive who should the most contribute to render pleasant that confinement which we were all equally obliged to share. Nor were those further advanced in life less anxious to contribute to the general satisfaction and entertainment.

After the more serious employment of reading each morning was concluded, we danced, we sung, we played at blind-man's-buff, battledore and shuttlecock, and many other games equally diverting and innocent; and when tired of them, drew our seats round the fire, while each one in turn told some merry story to divert the company.

At last, after having related all that we could recollect worth reciting, and being rather at a loss what to say next, a sprightly girl in company proposed that every one should relate the history of their own lives; 'and it must be strange indeed,' added she, 'if that will not help us out of this difficulty, and furnish conversation for some days longer; and by that time, perhaps, the frost will break, the snow will melt, and set us all at liberty. But let it break when it will, I make a law, that no one shall go from Meadow Hall till they have told their own history: so take notice, ladies and gentlemen, take notice, everybody, what you have to trust to. And because,' continued she, 'I will not be unreasonable, and require more from you than you can perform, I will give all you who may perhaps have forgotten what passed so many years ago, at the beginning of your lives, two days to recollect and digest your story; by which time if you do not produce something pretty and entertaining, we will never again admit you to dance or play among us.' All this she spoke with so good-humoured a smile, that every one was delighted with her, and promised to do their best to acquit themselves to her satisfaction; whilst some (the length of whose lives had not rendered them forgetful of the transactions which had passed) instantly began their memoirs, as they called them: and really some related their narratives with such spirit and ingenuity, that it quite distressed us older ones, lest we should disgrace ourselves when it should fall to our turns to hold forth. However, we were all determined to produce something, as our fair directress ordered. Accordingly, the next morning I took up my pen, to endeavour to draw up some kind of a history, which might satisfy my companions in confinement. I took up my pen, it is true, and laid the paper before me; but not one word toward my appointed task could I proceed. The various occurrences of my life were such as, far from affording entertainment, would, I was certain, rather afflict; or, perhaps, not interesting enough for that, only stupefy, and render them more weary of the continuation of the frost than they were before I began my narration. Thus circumstanced, therefore, although by myself, I broke silence by exclaiming, 'What a task his this sweet girl imposed upon me! One which I shall never be able to execute to my own satisfaction or her amusement. The adventures of my life (though deeply interesting to myself) will be insipid and unentertaining to others, especially to my young hearers: I cannot, therefore, attempt it.' - 'Then write mine, which may be more diverting,' said a little squeaking voice, which sounded as if close to me. I started with surprise, not knowing any one to be near me; and looking round, could discover no object from whom it could possibly proceed, when casting my eyes upon the ground, in a little hole under the skirting-board, close by the fire, I discovered the head of a mouse peeping out. I arose with a design to stop the hole with a cork, which happened to lie on the table by me; and I was surprised to find that it did not run away, but suffered me to advance quite close, and then only retreated a little into the hole, saying in the same voice as before, 'Will you write my history?' You may be sure that I was much surprised to be so addressed by such an animal; but, ashamed of discovering any appearance of astonishment, lest the mouse should suppose it had frightened me, I answered with the utmost composure, that I would write it willingly if it would dictate to me. 'Oh, that I will do,' replied the mouse, 'if you will not hurt me.' - 'Not for the world,' returned I; 'come, therefore, and sit upon my table, that I may hear more distinctly what you have to relate.' It instantly accepted my invitation, and with all the nimbleness of its species, ran up the side of my chair, and jumped upon my table; when, getting into a box of wafers, it began as follows.

But, before I proceed to relate my new little companion's history, I must beg leave to assure my readers that, in earnest, I never heard a mouse speak in all my life; and only wrote the following narrative as being far more entertaining, and not less instructive, than my own life would have been: and as it met with the high approbation of those for whom it was written, I have sent it to Mr. Marshall, for him to publish it, if he pleases, for the equal amusement of his little customers.

Dorothy Kilner

PART I.

Like all other newborn animals, whether of the human, or any other species, I can not pretend to remember what passed during my infant days. The first circumstance I can recollect was my mother's addressing me and my three brothers, who all lay in the same nest, in the following words:-'I have, my children, with the greatest difficulty, and at the utmost hazard of my life, provided for you all to the present moment; but the period is arrived, when I can no longer pursue that method: snares and traps are everywhere set for me, nor shall I, without infinite danger, be able to procure sustenance to support my own existence, much less can I find sufficient for you all; and, indeed, with pleasure I behold it as no longer necessary, since you are of age now to provide and shift for yourselves; and I doubt not but your agility will enable you to procure a very comfortable livelihood. Only let me give you this one caution - never (whatever the temptation may be) appear often in the same place; if you do, however you may flatter yourselves to the contrary, you will certainly at last be destroyed.' So saying, she stroked us all with her fore paw as a token of her affection, and then hurried away, to conceal from us the emotions of her sorrow, at thus sending us into the wide world.

She was no sooner gone, than the thought of being our

own directors so charmed our little hearts, that we presently forgot our grief at parting from our kind parent; and, impatient to use our liberty, we all set forward in search of some food, or rather some adventure, as our mother had left us victuals more than sufficient to supply the wants of that day. With a great deal of difficulty, we clambered up a high wall on the inside of a wainscot, till we reached the story above that we were born in, where we found it much easier to run round within the skirting-board, than to ascend any higher.

While we were there, our noses were delightfully regaled with the scent of the most delicate food that we had ever smelt; we were anxious to procure a taste of it likewise, and after running round and round the room a great many times, we at last discovered a little crack, through which we made our entrance. My brother Longtail led the way; I followed; Softdown came next; but Brighteyes would not be prevailed upon to venture. The apartment which we entered was spacious and elegant; at least, differed so greatly from anything we had seen, that we imagined it the finest place upon earth. It was covered all over with a carpet of various colours, that not only concealed some bird-seeds which we came to devour, but also for some time prevented our being discovered; as we were of much the same hue with many of the flowers on the carpet. At last a little girl, who was at work in the room, by the side of her mamma, shrieked out as if violently hurt. Her mamma begged to know the cause of her sudden alarm. Upon which she called out, 'A mouse! a mouse! I saw one under the chair!' 'And if you did, my dear,' replied her mother, 'is that any reason for your behaving so ridiculously? If there were twenty mice, what harm could they possibly do? You may easily hurt and destroy then,; but, poor little things! they cannot, if they would, hurt you.' 'What, could they not bite me?' inquired the child. 'They may, indeed, be able to do that; but you may be very sure that they have no such inclination,' rejoined the mother. 'A mouse is one of the most timorous things in the world; every noise alarms it: and though it chiefly lives by plunder, it appears as if punished by its fears for the mischiefs which it commits among our property. It is therefore highly ridiculous to pretend to be alarmed at the sight of a creature that would run from the sound of your voice, and wishes never to come near you, lest, as you are far more able, you should also be disposed to hurt it.' 'But I am sure, madam,' replied the little girl, whose name I afterwards heard was Nancy, 'they do not always run away; for one day, as Miss Betsy Kite was looking among some things which she had in her box, a mouse jumped out and ran up her frock sleeve - she felt it quite up on her arm.' 'And what became of it then?' inquired the mother. 'It jumped down again,' replied Nancy, 'and got into a little hole in the window-seat; and Betsy did not see it again.' 'Well, then, my dear,' resumed the lady, 'what harm did it do her? Is not that a convincing proof of what I say, that you have no cause to be afraid of them, and that it is very silly to be so? It is certainly foolish to be afraid of any thing, unless it threatens us with immediate danger; but to pretend to be so at a mouse, and such like inoffensive things, is a degree of weakness that I can by no means suffer any of my children to indulge.' 'May I then, madam,' inquired the child, 'be afraid of cows and horses, and such great beasts as those?' 'Certainly not,' answered her mother, 'unless they are likely to hurt you. If a cow or an horse runs after you, I would have you fear them so much as to get out of the way; but if they are quietly walking or grazing in a field, then to fly from them, as if you thought they would eat you instead of the grass, is most absurd, and discovers great want of sense. I once knew a young lady, who, I believe, thought it looked pretty to be terrified at everything, and scream if dog or even a mouse looked at her: but most severely was she punished for her folly, by several very disagreeable accidents she by those means brought upon herself.

'One day when she was drinking tea in a large company, on the door being opened, a small Italian greyhound walked into the drawing-room. She happened to be seated near the mistress of the dog, who was making tea: the dog, therefore, walked toward her, in order to be by his favourite; but, upon his advancing near her, she suddenly jumped up, without considering what she was about, overturned the water-urn, the hot iron of which rolling out, set fire to her clothes, which instantly blazed up, being only muslin, and burnt her arms, face, and neck, most dreadfully: she was so much hurt as to be obliged to be put immediately to bed; nor did she recover enough to go abroad for many months. Now, though every one was sorry for her sufferings, who could possibly help blaming her for her ridiculous behaviour, as it was entirely owing to her own folly that she was so hurt? When she was talked to upon the subject, she pleaded for her excuse, that she was so frightened she did not know what she did, nor whither she was going; but as she thought that the dog was coming to her she could not help jumping up, to get out of his way. Now what ridiculous arguing was this! Why could not she help it? And if the dog had really been going to her, what harm would it have done? Could she suppose that the lady whose house she was at, would have suffered a beast to walk about the house loose, and go into company, if he was apt to bite and hurt people? Or why should she think he would more injure her, than those he had before passed by? But the real case was, she did not think at all; if she had given herself time for that, she could not have acted so ridiculously. Another time, when she was walking, from the same want of reflection, she very nearly drowned herself. She was passing over a bridge, the outside rails of which were in some places broken down: while she was there, some cows, which a man was driving, met her: immediately, without minding whither she went, she shrieked out, and at the same time jumped on one side just where the rail happened to be broken, and down she fell into the river; nor was it without the greatest difficulty that she was taken out time enough to save her life. However, she caught a violent cold and fever, and was again, by her own foolish fears, confined to her bed for some weeks. Another accident she once met with, which though not quite so bad as the two former, yet might have been attended with fatal consequences. She was sitting in a window, when a wasp happened to fly toward her; she hastily drew back her head, and broke the pane of glass behind her, some of which stuck in her neck. It bled prodigiously; but a surgeon happily being present, made some application to it, which prevented its being followed by any other ill effects than only a few days weakness, occasioned by the loss of blood. Many other misfortunes of the like kind she frequently experienced; but these which I have now related may serve to convince you how extremely absurd it is for people to give way to and indulge themselves in such groundless apprehensions, and, by being afraid when there is no danger, subject themselves to real misfortunes and most fatal accidents. And if being afraid of cows, dogs, and wasps (all of which, if they please, can certainly hurt us) is so ridiculous, what must be the folly of those people who are terrified at a little silly mouse, which never was known to hurt anybody?'

Here the conversation was interrupted by the entrance of some gentlemen and ladies; and we having enjoyed a very fine repast under one of the chairs during the time that the mother and daughter had held the above discourse, on the chairs being removed for some of the visitors to sit upon, we thought it best to retire: highly pleased with our meal, and not less with the kind goodwill which the lady had, we thought, expressed towards us. We related to our brother Brighteyes all that had passed, and assured him he had no reason to apprehend any danger from venturing himself with us. Accordingly he promised, if such was the case, that the next time we went and found it safe, if we would return back and call him, he would certainly accompany us. 'In the mean time, do pray, Nimble,' said he, addressing himself to me, 'come with me to some other place, for I long to taste some more delicate food than our mother has provided for us: besides, as perhaps it may be a long while before we shall be strong enough to bring anything away with us, we had better leave that, in case we should ever be prevented from going abroad to seek for fresh supplies.' 'Very true,' replied I; 'what you say is quite just and wise, therefore I will with all my heart attend you now, and see what we can find.' So saying, we began to climb; but not without difficulty, for very frequently the bits of mortar which we stepped upon gave way beneath our feet, and tumbled us down together with them lower than when we first set off. However, as we were very light, we were not much hurt by our falls; only indeed poor Brighteyes, by endeavouring to save himself, caught by his nails on a rafter, and tore one of them from off his right fore-foot, which was very sore and inconvenient. At length we surmounted all difficulties, and, invited by a strong scent of plum-cake, entered a closet, where we found a fine large one, quite whole and entire. We immediately set about making our way into it, which we easily effected, as it was most deliciously nice, and not at all hard to our teeth.

Brighteyes, who had not before partaken of the bird-seed, was overjoyed at the sight. He almost forgot the pain of his foot, and soon buried himself withinside the cake; whilst I, who had pretty well satisfied my hunger before, only ate a few of the crumbs, and then went to take a survey of the adjoining apartment. I crept softly under the door of the closet into a room, as large as that which I had before been in, though not so elegantly furnished; for, instead of being covered with a carpet, there was only a small one round the bed; and near the fire was a cradle, with a cleanly-looking woman sitting by it, rocking it with her foot, whilst at the same time she was combing the head of a little boy about four years old. In the middle of the room stood a table, covered with a great deal of litter; and in one corner was the little girl whom I had before seen with her mamma, crying and sobbing as if her heart would break. As I made not the least noise at my entrance, no one observed me for some time; so creeping under one of the beds, I heard the following discourse: -

'It does not signify, miss,' said the woman, who I found was the children's nurse, 'I never will put up with such behaviour: you know that I always do everything for you when you speak prettily; but to be ordered to dress you in such a manner, is what I never will submit to:

and you shall go undressed all day before I will dress you, unless you ask me as you ought to do.' Nancy made no reply, but only continued crying. 'Aye! you may cry and sob as much as you please,' said the nurse; 'I do not care for that: I shall not dress you for crying and roaring, but for being good and speaking with civility.' Just as she said these words, the door opened, and in came the lady whom I before saw, and whose name I afterwards found was Artless. As soon as she entered, the nurse addressed her, saying, 'Pray, madam, is it by your desire that Miss Nancy behaves so rudely, and bids me dress her directly, and change the buckles in her shoes, or else she will slap my face? Indeed she did give me a slap upon my hand; so I told her, that I would not dress her at all; for really, madam, I thought you would not wish me to do it, whilst she behaved so; and I took the liberty of putting her to stand in the corner.' 'I do not think,' replied Mrs. Artless, 'that she deserves to stand in the room at all, or in the house either, if she behaves in that manner: if she does not speak civilly when she wants to be assisted, let her go without help, and see what will become of her then. I am quite ashamed of you, Nancy! I could not have thought you would behave so; but since you have, I promise that you shall not be dressed today, or have any assistance given you, unless you speak in a very different manner.'

Whilst Mrs. Artless was talking, nurse went out of the room. Mrs. Artless then took her seat by the cradle, and looking into it, found the child awake, and I saw her take out a fine little girl, about five months old: she then continued her discourse, saying, 'Look here, Nancy, look at this little baby, see how unable it is to help itself; were we to neglect attending to it, what do you think would become of it? Suppose I were now to put your sister upon the floor, and there leave her, tell me what do you think she could do, or what would become of her?' Nancy sobbed out, that she would die. 'And pray, my dear,' continued Mrs. Artless, 'if we were to leave you to yourself, what would become of you? It is true, you talk and run about better than Polly: but not a bit better could you provide for, or take care of yourself. Could you buy or dress your own victuals? could you light your own fire? could you clean your own house, or open and shut the doors and windows? could you make your own clothes, or even put them on without some assistance, when made? And who do you think will do anything for you, if you are not good, and do not speak civilly? Not I, I promise you, neither shall nurse, nor any of the servants; for though I pay them wages to help to do my business for me, I never want them to do anything unless they are desired in a pretty manner. Should you like, if when I want you to pick up my scissors, or do any little job, I were to say, "Pick up my scissors this moment, or I will slap your face?" Should not you think that it sounded very cross and disagreeable?' 'Yes, madam,' replied Nancy. 'Then why,' rejoined Mrs. Artless, 'should you speak cross to anybody, particularly to servants and poor people? for to behave so to them, is not only cross, but insolent and proud: it is as if you thought that because they are rather poorer, they are not so good as yourself, whereas, I assure you, poverty makes no difference in the merit of people; for those only are deserving of respect who are truly good; and a beggar who is virtuous, is far better than a prince who is wicked.' I was prevented from hearing any more of this very just discourse, by the little boy's opening the door and letting in a cat; which, though it was the first that I had ever seen in my life, I was certain was the same destructive animal to our race, which I had frequently heard my mother describe. I therefore made all possible haste back to the closet, and warning Brighteyes of our danger, we instantly returned by the same way which we came, to our two brothers, whom we found waiting for us, and wondering at our long absence. We related to them the dainty cheer which we had met with, and agreed to conduct them thither in the evening. Accordingly, as soon as it grew towards dusk, we climbed up the wall, and all four together attacked the plum-cake, which no one had touched since we left it; but scarcely had we all seated ourselves round it, than on a sudden the closet-door opened, and a woman entered. Away we all scampered as fast as possible, but poor Brighteyes, who could not move quite so fast on account of his sore toe, and who likewise having advanced farther into the cake, was discovered before he could reach the crack by which we entered. The woman, who had a knife in her hand, struck at him with it, at the same time exclaiming, 'Bless me, nurse, here is a mouse in the closet!' Happily, she missed her aim, and he only received a small wound on the tip of his tail. This interruption sadly alarmed us, and it was above an hour before we could have courage to venture back, when finding everything quiet, except Mrs. Nurse's singing to her child, we again crept out, and once more surrounded the cake. We continued without any further alarm till we were perfectly satisfied, and then retired to a little distance behind the wainscot, determined there to sleep, and to breakfast on the cake the next day.

Early in the morning I waked, and calling my brothers, we all marched forward, and soon arrived at the delightful cake, where we highly enjoyed ourselves without the least disturbance, till our appetites were fully satisfied. We then retired, took a little run round some other parts of the house, but met with nothing worth relating. At noon we again made our way into the closet, intending to dine on the dish on which we breakfasted; but, to our no small mortification, the delicious dainty was removed. This you may be sure was a sad disappointment; yet as we were not extremely hungry, we had time to look about for more. We were not long in finding it; for upon the same shelf from which the cake was removed, there was a round tin box, the lid of which was not quite close shut down; into this we all crept, and were highly regaled with some nice lumps of sugar. But it would be endless to enumerate all the various repasts which we met with in this closet, sometimes terrified by the entrance of people, and sometimes comfortably enjoying ourselves without alarm: it is sufficient to inform you, that, unmindful of our mother's advice, we continued to live upon the contents of the same cupboard for above a week; when, one evening, as we were as usual hastening to find our suppers, Softdown, who happened to be first, ran eagerly to a piece of cheese, which he saw hanging before him. 'Come along,' said he, 'here is some nice cheese, it smells most delightfully good!' Just as he spoke these words, before any of us came up to him, a little wooden door on a sudden dropped down, and hid him and the cheese from our sight.

It is impossible to describe our consternation and surprise upon this occasion, which was greatly increased when we advanced near the place, at seeing him (through some little wire bars) confined in a small box, without any visible way for him to get out, and hearing him in the most moving accents beg us to assist him in procuring his liberty. We all ran round and round his place of confinement several times; but not the least crack or opening could we discover, except through the bars, which being of iron, it was impossible for us to break or bend. At length we determined to try to gnaw through the wood-work close at the edge, which being already some little distance from one of the bars, we hoped, by making the opening a little wider, he would escape: accordingly we all began, he on the inside, and we all on the out, and by our diligence had made some very considerable progress, when we were interrupted by the entrance of Mrs. Nurse with the child in her arms.

Upon the sight of her, though much grieved to leave our brother in his distress, yet fearing instant death would be the fate of all of us if we stayed, to preserve our own existence, we retired as quick as possible, but not without her seeing some of us, for we heard her say to herself, or to the babe in her arms, 'I declare, this closet swarms with mice, they spoil everything one puts here.' Then taking up the box in which was poor Softdown (and which I afterwards learned was called a trap) she carried it into the room. I crept softly after her, to see what would be the fate of my beloved brother. But what words can express my horror, when I saw her holding it in one hand close to the candle, whilst in the other she held the child, singing to her with the utmost composure, and bidding her to look at the mousy! mousy!

What were the actions or sensations of poor Softdown at that dreadful moment I know not: but my own anguish, which it is impossible to describe, was still augmented every moment by seeing her shake the trap almost topsy-turvy, then blow through the trap at one end, at which times I saw the dear creature's tail come out between the wires on the contrary side, as he was

Dorothy Kilner

striving, I suppose, to retreat from her. At length, after she had thus tortured him for some time, she set the trap on the table, so close to a large fire, that I am sure he must have been much incommoded by the heat, and began to undress her child.

Then hearing somebody go by the door, she cried out, 'Who is there? is it you, Betty? if it is, I wish you would come and take down the mouse-trap, for I have caught a mouse.' Betty instantly obeyed her call, and desired to know what she wanted. 'I want you to take down the mouse-trap,' she replied, 'for I cannot leave the child. I am glad that I have got it, I am sure, for the closet swarms so, there is no such thing as bearing it. They devour everything: I declare they have eaten up a whole pound of sugar, which cost me elevenpence, sugar is now so monstrously dear! indeed the man made a favour to let me have it for that; only, he said, as our family were good customers, and I was but a servant, he would take no more. And enough too I thought it was, to have only a penny back in change out of a whole shilling for one pound of sugar: and then to think of the poison mice to have it all; but I will break their filthy necks. Do, Betty, pray take the trap down, and return with it as soon as you can, and I will set it again: for I dare say I shall catch another before I go to bed, for I heard some more rustling among the things.' 'O lauk!' replied Betty, 'yon do not think that I will take down the trap, do you? I would not touch it for twenty pounds. I am always frightened, and ready to die at the sight of a mouse. Once, when I was a girl, I had one thrown in my face, and ever since I have always been scared out of my wits at them; and if ever I see one running loose, as I did one night in the closet below stairs, where the candles are kept, I scream as if I was being killed.' 'Why then,' answered Nurse, 'I think you behave like a great fool, for what harm could a mouse do to you?' 'O la! I hate them,' returned she, and then ran away without the trap. Greatly was I rejoiced at her departure, as I hoped that, by some means, Softdown might still be able to make his escape. But, alas! no such good fortune attended him. Some person again passing the door, Nurse once more called out, 'Who is there? John is it you?' 'Yes,' replied a man's voice. 'Then do you step in, will you, for a moment?' rejoined Mrs. Nurse: and instantly entered a man whom I had never before seen. 'What do you want, Nurse?' said he. 'I only want to get rid of a mouse,' returned she; 'and, do you know, Betty is such a fool that she is afraid of taking it, and I want the trap to set it again, for they swarm here like bees in a hive, one can have no peace for them: they devour and spoil every thing; I say sometimes that I believe they will eat me up at last.' While she was saying this, John took the trap in his hand, held it up once more to the candle, then taking a piece of thread out of a paper, that lay bound round with a dirty blue ribbon upon the table, he shook the trap about till he got my brother's tail through the wires, when catching hold of it, he tied the thread tight round it and dragged him by it to the door of the trap, which he opened, and took him out, suspending the weight of his body upon his tail.

Softdown, who till the thread was tied had patiently continued perfectly quiet, could no longer support the pain without dismal cries and anguish: he squeaked as loud as his little throat would let him, exerting at the same time the utmost of his strength to disengage himself. But in such a position, with his head downward, in vain were all his efforts to procure relief; and the barbarous monster who held him discovered not the smallest emotions of pity for his sufferings. Oh!

how at that moment did I abhor my own existence, and wish that I could be endowed with size and strength sufficient, at once both to rescue him, and severely punish his tormentors. But my wish was ineffectual, and I had the inexpressible affliction of seeing the inhuman wretch hold him down upon the hearth, whilst, without remorse, he crushed him beneath his foot, and then carelessly kicked him into the ashes, saying, 'There! The cat will smell it out when she comes up.' My very blood runs cold within me at the recollection of seeing Softdown's as it spurted from beneath the monster's foot; whilst the crunch of his bones almost petrified me with horror. At length, however, recollecting the impossibility of restoring my beloved brother to life, and the danger of my own situation, I, with trembling feet and palpitating heart, crept softly back to my remaining two brothers, who were impatiently expecting me behind the closet. There I related to them the horrid scene which had passed before my eyes, whilst the anguish it caused in their gentle bosoms far exceeds my power to describe.

After having mingled our lamentations for some time, I thus addressed them: 'We have this night, my brothers, tasted the severest affliction in the cruel death of our dear brother, companion, and friend; let us not, however, only mourn his loss, but also gather wisdom from our misfortune, and return to that duty which we have hitherto neglected. Recollect, my dear friends, what were the last words which our good mother spoke to us at parting. She charged us, upon no account, for no temptation whatever, to return frequently to the same place: if we did, she forewarned us that death and ruin would certainly await us. But in what manner have we obeyed this her kind advice? We have not even so much as once recollected it since she left us;

or, if we thought of it for a moment, we foolishly despised it as unnecessary. Now, therefore, we sincerely feel the consequence of our disobedience; and, though our sufferings are most distressing, yet we must confess that we amply deserve them. Let us therefore, my brothers, instantly fly from a place which has already cost us the life of our beloved Softdown, lest we should all likewise fall a sacrifice to our disobedience.' - And here the writer cannot help observing how just were the reflections of the mouse on the crime which they had been guilty of; and begs every reader will be careful to remember the fatal consequences that attended their disobedience of their mother's advice, since they may be assured that equal if not the same misfortune will always attend those who refuse to pay attention to the advice of their parents. But, to return to the history.

To this proposal (continued the mouse) my brothers readily agreed; and we directly descended to the place we were in when we discovered the crack that led us to the room in which we feasted on bird-seed. Here we determined to wait, and when the family were all quiet in bed, to go forth in search of provision, as we began to be rather hungry, not having eaten anything a long while. Accordingly we stayed till after the clock struck twelve, when peeping out, we saw that the room was empty: we then ventured forth, and found several seeds, though not enough to afford a very ample meal for three of us.

After we had cleared the room, we again returned to our hiding-place, where we continued till after the family had finished their breakfast. They all then went to take a walk in the garden, and we stepped out to pick up the crumbs which had fallen from the table.

Whilst we were thus employed, at a distance from our place of retreat, we were alarmed by the entrance of two boys, who appeared to be about twelve or thirteen years of age. We directly ran towards the crack; but alas! we were not quick enough to escape their observation; for, seeing us, they both at once exclaimed, 'Some mice! some mice!' and at the same time took off their hats, and threw at us. Longtail happily eluded the blow, and safely got home, but poor Brighteyes and myself were less fortunate; and though we for a considerable time, by our quickness, prevented their catching us, at length, being much disabled by a blow that one of them gave me with a book which he threw at me, I was unable any longer to run, and hobbling very slowly across the room, he picked me up. At the same moment Brighteyes was so entangled in a handkerchief which the other boy tossed over him, that he likewise was taken prisoner. Our little hearts now beat quick with fear of those tortures we expected to receive; nor were our apprehensions lessened by hearing the boys consult what they should do with us, 'I,' said one, 'will throw mine into the pond, and see how he will swim out again.' 'And I,' said the other, 'will keep mine and tame it.' 'But where will you keep it?' inquired his companion. 'Oh,' replied he, 'I will keep it under a little pan till I can get a house made for it.' He then, holding me by the skin at the back of my neck, ran with me into the kitchen to fetch a pan. Here I was not only threatened with death by three or four of the servants, who all blamed Master Peter for keeping me; but likewise two or three cats came round him, rubbing themselves backward and forward against his legs, and then standing upon their hind feet to endeavour to make themselves high enough to reach me. At last, taking a pan in his hand, he returned to his brother with one of the cats following him. Immediately upon our entrance, the boy exclaimed, 'Oh, now I know what I will do: I will tie a piece of string to its tail, and teach the cat to jump for it.' No sooner did this thought present itself than it was put into practice, and I again was obliged to sustain the shocking sight of a brother put to the torture. I, in the mean time, was placed upon the table, with a pan put over me, in which there was a crack, so that I could see as well as hear all that passed: and from this place it was that I beheld my beloved Brighteyes suspended at one end of a string by his tail; one while swinging backward and forward, at another pulled up and down, then suffered to feel his feet on the ground, and again suddenly snatched up as the cat advanced, then twisted round and round as fast as possible at the full length of the string: in short, it is impossible to describe all his sufferings of body, or my anguish of mind. At length a most dreadful conclusion was put to them, by the entrance of a gentleman booted and spurred, with a whip in his hand. 'What in the world, Charles!' said he, as he came in, 'are you about? What have you got there?' 'Only a mouse, sir,' replied the boy. 'He is teaching the cat to jump, sir,' said Peter, 'that is all.'

Brighteyes then gave a fresh squeak from the violence of his pain. The gentleman then turning hastily round, exclaimed eagerly, 'What, is it alive?' 'Yes, sir,' said the boy. 'And how can you, you wicked, naughty, cruel boy,' replied the gentleman, 'take delight in thus torturing a little creature that never did you any injury? Put it down this moment,' said he, at the same time giving him a severe stroke with his horse-whip across that hand by which he held my brother. 'Let it go directly,' and again repeated the blow: the boy let go the string, and Brighteyes fell to the ground; and was instantly snapped up by the cat, who growling, ran away with him in her mouth, and, I suppose, put a conclusion to his miseries and life together, as I never from that moment have heard any account of him.

As soon as he was thus taken out of the room, the gentleman sat down, and, taking hold of his son's hand, thus addressed him: 'Charles, I had a much better opinion of you, than to suppose you were capable of so much cruelty. What right, I desire to know, have you to torment any living creature? If it is only be cause you are larger, and so have it in your power, I beg you will consider, how you would like, that either myself, or some great giant, as much larger than you as you are bigger than the mouse, should hurt and torment you? And I promise you, the smallest creature can feel as acutely as you, nay, the smaller they are, the more susceptible are they of pain, and the sooner they are hurt: a less touch will kill a fly than a man, consequently a less wound will cause it pain; and the mouse which you have now been swinging by the tail over the cat's mouth, has not, you may assure yourself, suffered less torment or fright than you would have done, had you been suspended by your leg, either over water, which would drown you, or over stones, where if you fell you must certainly be dashed to pieces. And yet you could take delight in thus torturing and distressing a poor inoffensive animal. Fie upon it, Charles! fie upon it! I thought you had been a better boy, and not such a cruel, naughty, wicked fellow.' 'Wicked!' repeated the boy, 'I do not think that I have been at all wicked.' 'But I think you have been extremely so,' replied his father; 'every action that is cruel, and gives pain to any living creature, is wicked, and is a sure sign of a bad heart. I never knew a man, who was cruel to animals, kind and compassionate towards his fellow-creatures: he might not perhaps treat them in the same shocking manner, because the laws of the land would severely punish him if he did; but if he is restrained from bad actions by no higher motive than fear of present punishment, his goodness cannot be very great. A good man, Charles, always takes delight in conferring happiness on all around him; nor would he offer the smallest injury to the meanest insect that was capable of feeling. 'I am sure,' said the boy, 'I have often seen you kill wasps, and spiders too; and it was but last week that you bought a mouse-trap yourself to catch mice in, although you are so angry now with me.' 'And pray,' resumed his father, 'did you ever see me torment as well as kill them? Or did I ever keep them in pain one moment longer than necessary? I am not condemning people for killing vermin and animals, provided they do it expeditiously, and put them to death with as little pain as possible; but it is putting them to needless torment and misery that I say is wicked. Had you destroyed the mouse with one blow, or rather given it to somebody else to destroy it (for I should not think a tender-hearted boy would delight in such operations himself), I would not have condemned you; but, to keep it hanging the whole weight of its body upon its tail, to swing it about, and, by that, to hold it terrifying over the cat's jaws, and to take pleasure in hearing it squeak, and seeing it struggle for liberty, is such unmanly, such detestable cruelty, as calls for my utmost indignation and abhorrence. But, since you think pain so very trifling an evil, try. Charles, how you like that,' said he, giving him at the same time some severe strokes with his horsewhip. The boy then cried, and called out, 'I do not like it at all, I do not like it at all.' 'Neither did the mouse,' replied his father, 'like at all to be tied to a string, and swung about by his tail: he did not like it, and told you so in a language which you perfectly well understood; but you would not attend to his cries; you thought it pleasure to hear it squeak, because you were bigger, and did not feel its torture. I am now bigger than you. and do not feel your pain. I therefore shall not yet leave off; as I hope it will teach you not to torment anything another time.' Just as he said these words, the boy, endeavouring to avoid the whip, ran against the table on which I was placed, and happily threw down the pan that confined me. I instantly seized the opportunity, jumped down, and once more escaped to the little hole by which I first entered. There I found my only brother waiting for me, and was again under the dreadful necessity of paining his tender heart with the recital of the sufferings which I had been witness to in our dear Brighteyes, as well as the imminent danger I myself had been exposed to. 'And, surely,' said I, 'we have again drawn this evil upon ourselves by our disobedience to our mother's advice; she, doubtless, intended that we should not continue in the same house long together; whereas from the day of her leaving us, we have never been in any other but this, which has occasioned us such heavy affliction. Therefore, upon no account, let us continue another night under this roof; but, as soon as the evening begins to grow dark enough to conceal us from the observation of any one, we will set off, and seek a lodging in some other place; and should any misfortune befall us on our passage, we shall at least have the consolation of thinking. that we were doing our duty by following the advice of our parent.' 'It is true,' said my brother, 'we have been greatly to blame; for the future we will be more careful of our conduct; but do, my dear Nimble,' continued he, 'endeavour to compose yourself, and take a little rest, after the pain and fatigue which you have gone through, otherwise you may be sick; and what will become of me, if any mischief should befall you? I shall then have no brother to converse with, no friend to advise me what to do.' Here he stopped, over-powered with his grief for the loss of our two murdered brothers, and with his tender solicitude for my welfare. I endeavoured all in my power to comfort him, and said I hoped that I should soon recover from the bruises I had received both from the boy's hat and book, as well as the pinches in my neck with his finger and thumb, by which he held me, and promised to compose myself. This promise I fulfilled by endeavouring to sleep; but the scene that I had so lately been witness to was too fresh in my imagination to suffer me to close my eyes: however, I kept for some time quiet.

The rest of the day we spent in almost total silence, having no spirits for conversation, our hearts being almost broken with anguish. When it grew toward evening, we agreed to find our way out of that detested house, and seek for some other habitation, which might be more propitious. But we found more difficulty in this undertaking than we were at all aware of; for though we could with tolerable ease go from room to room within the house, still, when we attempted to quit it, we found it every way surrounded with so thick a brick wall, that it was impossible for us to make our way through it: we therefore ran round and round it several times, searching for some little crevice through which we might escape; but all to no purpose, not the least crack could we discover: and we might have continued there till this time, had we not at length, after the family were in bed, resolved to venture through one of the apartments into the hall, and so creep out under the house door. But the dangers we exposed ourselves to in this expedition were many and great; we knew that traps were set for us about the house, and where they might chance to be placed we could not tell. I had likewise been eye-witness to no less than four cats, who might, for ought we knew to the contrary, at that hour of darkness, be prowling in search of some of our unhappy species.

But, in spite of every difficulty and hazard, we determined to venture rather than continue in opposition to our mother's commands; and, to reward our obedience, we escaped with trembling hearts, unobserved, at least unmolested, by any one. And now, for the first time since our birth, we found ourselves exposed to the inclemency of the weather. The night was very dark and tempestuous; the rain poured down in torrents; and the wind blew so exceedingly high, that, low upon the ground as we were, it was with difficulty that we could keep our legs: added to which, even step we took, we were in water up to our stomachs. In this wretched condition we knew not which way to turn ourselves, or where to seek for shelter. The spattering of the rain, the howling of the wind, together with the rattling and shaking of the trees, all contributed to make such a noise as rendered it impossible for us to hear whether any danger was approaching us or not.

In this truly melancholy situation we waded on for a considerable time, till at length we reached a small house, and very easily gained admittance through a pretty large hole on one side of the door. Most heartily did we rejoice at finding ourselves once more under shelter from the cold and rain, and for some time only busied ourselves in drying our hair, which was as thoroughly wet as if we had been served as the boy threatened my brother Brighteyes, and we had really been drawn through a pond. After we had done this, and had a little rested ourselves, we began to look about in search of food, but we could find nothing. except a few crumbs of bread and cheese in a man's coat pocket, and a piece of tallow-candle stuck on the top of a tinder-box. This, however, though not such delicate eating as we had been used to, yet served to satisfy our present hunger; and we had just finished the candle when we were greatly alarmed by the sight of a human hand (for we mice can see a little in the dark) feeling about the very chair on which we stood. We jumped down in an instant, and hid ourselves in a little hole behind a black trunk that stood in one corner of the room.

We then heard very distinctly a man say, 'Betty, did you not put the candle by the bedside?' 'Yes, that I am very sure I did,' replied a female voice. 'I thought so,' answered the man; 'but I am sure it is not here now. Tom! Tom! Tom!' continued he. 'What, father?' replied a boy, starting up, 'what is the matter?' 'Why, do you know anything of the candle? I cannot find it, my dear, and I want it sadly, for I fancy it is time we should be up and be jogging. Dost know any thing of it, my lad?' 'Not I, truly, father,' said the boy, 'I only know that I saw mother stick it in the box-lid last night, and put it upon the chair, which she set by the bedside, after you had put your clothes upon the back of it; I know I saw her put it there, so it must be there now, I fancy.' 'Well, I cannot find it,' replied the father; so we must e'en get up in the dark, for I am sure it must be time.' The father and son then both dressed themselves, and the man, taking a shilling out of his pocket, laid it upon the chair, saying at the same time, 'There, Betty. I have left a shilling for you; take care it does not go after the candle, for where that is I cannot tell any more than the carp at the bottom of the squire's fish-pond.' He then unlocked the door, and went away, accompanied by his son.

After their departure, we again came out, and took another walk round the room, and found our way into a little cupboard, which we had not before observed. Here we discovered half a loaf of bread, a piece of cold pudding, a lump of salt butter, some soft sugar in a basin, and a fine large slice of bacon. On these dainties we feasted very amply, and agreed that we should again hide ourselves behind the black trunk all day, and at night, when the family were in bed, return to take another meal on the plenty of nice provision which we so happily discovered. Accordingly, we crept back just as the woman went to fill her teakettle at a pump, which stood between her house and the next neighbour's. When she returned, she put it upon the fire she had just lit, and, taking a pair of bellows in her hand, sat down to blow it.

While she was so employed, a young gentleman, about ten years of age, very genteelly dressed, entered the room, and in a familiar manner asked her how she did. 'I am very well, thank you, my dear,' replied she: 'and pray, Master George, how does your mamma and papa do; and all your brothers and sisters?' 'They are all very well, thank you,' returned the boy: 'And I am come to bring you a slice of cake, which my grandpapa gave me yesterday.' Then throwing his arms round her neck, he went on saying, 'Oh! my dear, dear Betty Flood, how I do love you! I would do anything in the world to serve you. I shall save all my Christmas-boxes to give to you; and when I am a man, I will give you a great deal of money. I wish you were a lady, and not so poor.' 'I am much obliged to you, my dear,' said she, 'for your kind good-wishes; but, indeed, love, I am very well contented with my station: I have a good husband, and three good children, and that is more than many a lady can say; and riches, Master George, unless people are good, and those one lives with are kind and obliging, will never make anybody happy. What comfort, now, do you think a body could ever have at Squire Stately's? I declare, if it was put to my choice, I would rather a thousand times be as I am. To be sure, they are very rich; but what of that? they cannot eat gold; neither can gold ease their hearts when they are bursting almost with pride and ill-nature. They say, indeed, that Madam Stately would be kind enough, if they would let her rest; but what with the Squire's drinking and swearing, and the young gentleman's extravagance, and her daughter's pride and quarrelling, she is almost tired out of her life. And so, Master George, I say I had rather be poor Betty Flood, with honest Abraham for my husband, than the finest lady in the land, if I must live at such a rate. To be sure, nobody can deny but that money is very desirable, and people that are rich can do many agreeable things which we poor ones cannot; but yet, for all that, money does not make people happy. Happiness, Master George, depends greatly upon people's own tempers and dispositions: a person who is fretful and cross will never be happy, though he should be made king of all England; and a person who is contented and good-humoured will never be wretched, though he should be as poor as a beggar. So never fret yourself, love, because Betty Flood is poor; for though I am poor, I am honest; and whilst my husband and I are happy enough to be blessed with health, and the use of our limbs, we can work for our living; and though we have no great plenty, still we have sufficient to support us. So pray, dear, eat your cake yourself, for I would not take it from you for ever so much.' They then disputed for some time who should have it: at last, George scuffled away from her, and put it into the closet, and then, nodding his head at her, ran away, saying, he must go to school that moment.

Betty Flood then ate her breakfast; and we heard her say something about the nasty mice, but what we could not make out, as she muttered softly to herself. She then came to the trunk behind which we lay, and taking out of it a roll of new linen, sat down to needlework. At twelve o'clock her husband and son returned; so moving her table out of the way, she made room for them at the fire, and, fetching the frying pan, dressed some rashers of the nice bacon we had before tasted in the cupboard. The boy, in the mean time, spread a cloth on the table, and placed the bread and cold pudding on it likewise: then, returning to the closet for their plates, he cried out, 'Lauk! father, here is a nice hunch of plum-cake; can you tell how it came?' 'Not I, indeed, Tom,' replied his father; 'I can tell no more than the carp at the bottom of the squire's fish-pond.' 'Oh, I will tell you.' said Mrs. Flood; 'I know how it came. Do you know, that dear child, Master George Kendall, brought it for me; he called as he went to school this morning. I told him I would not have it; but the dear little soul popped it into the cupboard, and ran away without it. Bless his little heart! I do think he is the sweetest child that ever was born. You may laugh at me for saying so; but I am sure I should have thought the same if I had not nursed him myself.' 'Indeed,' replied her husband, 'I do not laugh at you for saying so, for I think so too, and so must everyone who knows him; for when young gentlemen behave as he does, everybody must love and admire them. There is nothing I would not do to help and serve that child, or any of his family; they always are so kind, and speak as civilly to us poor folk as if we were the first lords or ladies in the land. I am sure, if it were needful, I would go through fire and water for their sakes; and so would every man in the parish, I dare say. But I wonder who would do as much to help Squire Stately or any of his family, if it was not that I should think it my duty (and an honest man ought always to do that, whether he likes it or not); but I say, if it was not that it would be my duty to help my fellow-creature, I would scarcely be at the trouble of stepping over the threshold to serve them, they are such a set of cross, good-for-nothing gentry. I declare, it was but as we came home to dinner now, that we saw Master Sam throwing sticks and stones at Dame Frugal's ducks, for the sake of seeing them waddle; and then, when they got to the pond, he sent his dog in after them to bark and frighten them out of their wits. And as I came by, nothing would serve him but throwing a great dab of mud all over the sleeve of my coat. So I said, "Why, Master Sam, you need not have done that; I did nothing to offend you; and however amusing you may think it to insult poor people, I assure you it is very wicked, and what no good person in the world would be guilty of." He then set up a great rude laugh, and I walked on and said no more. But if all gentlefolk were to behave like that family, I had rather be poor as I am, than have all their riches, if that would make me act like them.' 'Very true, Abraham,' replied his wife, 'that is what I say, and what I told Master George this morning; for to be poor, if people do not become so through their own extravagance, is no disgrace to any body: but to be haughty, cruel, cross, and mischievous, is a disgrace to all who are so, let their rank be as exalted as it may.'

Here the conversation was interrupted by the entrance of a man, who begged Mr. Flood to assist him in unloading his cart of flour, as his man was gone out, and he could not do it by himself. 'Well, I will come and help you, with all my heart,' said Flood; 'and so shall Tom too: will you, my lad? I cannot live without help myself; and if I do not assist others, I am sure I shall not deserve any when I want it.' So saying, he left his house; and his wife, after cleaning and putting in their proper places those things which had been used at dinner, again sat down to her sewing.

Soon after the clock had struck six, the man and his son returned; and, sitting round the fire, they passed the evening in social conversation, till they went to bed, which was a little after eight; and they convinced me, by their talk and behaviour, that happiness in this world depends far more upon the temper and disposition of the heart, than upon any external possessions; and that virtue, and a desire to be useful to others, afford far greater satisfaction and peace of mind than any riches and grandeur can possibly supply without such necessary qualifications. After they were all fallen asleep, we crept out; and, leaving the candle unmolested, which was again placed on the tinder-box by the bed-side, we hastened into the closet, where we regaled heartily, and devoured that part of the plum-cake which Tom had very generously left for his sister Polly, who we found was expected home the next day.

We then retired to our safe retreat, and thought we might venture to stay for one more night's provisions without running any danger from our too frequent return to the same place. But in the morning we found our scheme frustrated; for, on the woman's going to the closet to get her breakfast, she observed the robbery which we had committed, and exclaimed, 'Some teasing mice have found their way into the closet: I will borrow neighbour Savewell's trap to-night, and catch some of the little toads; that I will!' After hearing this, it would have been madness to make any further attempts: we therefore agreed to watch for an opportunity, and escape on the very first that offered. Accordingly, about noon, when Mrs. Flood was busily employed in making some pancakes, we slipped by her unobserved, and crept out at the same hole by which we first entered. But no sooner were we in the open road, than we repented our haste, and wished that we had continued where we were till the darkness of the night might better have concealed us from the observation of anyone. We crept as close to the wall of the house (as far as it reached, which was but a few paces) as we possibly could, and then stepped into a little ditch, which we were soon obliged to leave again, as the water ran in some parts of it almost up to the edge.

At length we reached a little cottage, which we were just entering, when a cat that was sleeping unnoticed by us upon a chair, jumped down, and would certainly have destroyed me (who happened to go first) had she not at the same moment tried to catch my brother, and by that means missed her aim, and so given us both an opportunity to escape, which we did by scrambling behind a brick that a child had been playing with by the side of the door. Fortunately, the brick lay too close to the house for the cat to get her paw behind it, so as to be able to reach us; though to avoid it we were obliged to use the greatest precaution, as she could thrust it in a little way, so that if we had gone one inch too near either end, she would certainly have dragged us out by her talons. In this dreadful situation did we spend some hours, incessantly moving from one end of the brick to the other; for the moment she had, by the

Dorothy Kilner

entrance of her paw at one end, driven us to the other, she stepped over, and again made us retreat. Think with what dreadful terror our little hearts must have been oppressed, to see our mortal enemy so closely watching us, expecting every moment when she shook the brick with her two forepaws in searching, and with her mouth endeavoured to lift it up, that she would be so far able to effect her purpose, as to make it impossible for us to escape her jaws. But, happily for us, it had somehow or other got so wedged that she could not move it to any distance; though it kept momentarily increasing our terrors, by shaking as she strove to turn it.

From this state of horror, however, we were at length delivered by a little boy of about two years old, who came out of the house, and taking the cat up round its body with both hands, tottered away with it, and shut the door.

Finding ourselves thus unexpectedly once more at liberty, we determined to make use of it, by seeking some safer retreat, at least, till night should better hide us from public view. Terrified almost out of our senses, we crept from behind the brick, and, after running a few yards, slipped under the folding doors of a barn, and soon concealed ourselves amidst a vast quantity of threshed corn. This appeared to us the most desirable retreat that we had yet found; not only as it afforded such immense plenty of food, but also as we could so easily hide ourselves from the observation of any one: beside, as it did not appear to be a dwelling-house, we could in security reside, free from any danger of traps, or the cruelty of man. We therefore congratulated each other, not more on account of the wonderful escape which we had, than upon our good fortune in coming to a Spot so blessed with peace and plenty.

After we were a little recovered from the fatigue of mind, as well as of body, which we had lately gone through, we regaled very heartily upon the corn that surrounded us, and then fell into a charming sleep, from which we were awakened the next morning by the sound of human voices. We very distinctly heard that of a boy, saying, 'Let us mix all the threshed corn with the rest that is not threshed, and that will make a fine fuss, and set John and Simon a swearing like troopers when they come and find all their labour lost, and that they must do all their work over again.' 'And do you think there is anything so agreeable in giving people trouble, and hearing them swear,' replied another voice, 'that you can wish to do it? For my part. I think it is so wicked a thing, that I hate to hear anybody guilty of it, much less would I be the cause of making them commit so great a sin; and as for giving them all their trouble over again, so far would it be from affording me any pleasure, that on the contrary it would give me great pain; for however you may think of it, Will, I assure you, it always gives me much uneasiness to see people labouring and working hard. I always think how much I should dislike to be obliged to do so myself, and therefore very sincerely pity those who must. On no account therefore will I do anything to add to their labour, or that shall give them unnecessary work.'

'Pooh!' answered Will, 'you are wonderfully wise; I, for my part, hate such super-abundant wisdom; I like to see folk fret, and stew, and scold, as our maids did last week when I cut the line, and let all the sheets, and gowns, and petticoats, and frocks, and shirts, and aprons, and caps, and what not, fall plump into the dirt. O! how I did laugh! and how they did mutter and scold! And do you know, that just as the wash ladies were wiping their coddled hands, and comforted themselves with the thought of their work being all over, and were going to sip their tea by the fireside, I put them all to the scout; and they were obliged to wash every rag over again. I shall never forget how cross they looked, nay, I verily believe Susan cried about it; and how I did laugh!'

'And pray,' rejoined the other boy, 'should you have laughed equally hearty if, after you had been at school all day, and had with much difficulty just got through all your writing, and different exercises, and were going to play, should you laugh, I say, if somebody was to run away with them all, and your master oblige you to do them all over again? Tell me, Will, should you laugh, or cry and look cross? And even that would not be half so bad for you, as it was for the maids to be obliged to wash their clothes over again; washing is very hard labour, and tires people sadly, and so does threshing too. It is very unkind, therefore, to give them such unnecessary trouble; and everything that is unkind, is wicked; and I would not do it upon any account, I assure you.' 'Then I assure you,' replied Will, 'you may let it alone; I can do it without your assistance.' He then began mixing the grain and the chaff together, the other boy strongly remonstrating against it, to which he paid no attention; and whilst he was so employed, two men, Simon and John, entered the barn.

'Why, how now, Master Billy,' said Simon; 'what are you about? What business have you to be here? You are always doing some mischief or other! I wish, with all my heart, that you were kept chained like a dog, and never suffered to be at liberty, for you do more harm in an hour, than a body can set right again in a month!' Will then took up hats full of the corn and chaff, and threw it in the two men's faces; afterwards taking up a flail, he gave Simon a blow across his back, saying, at the same time, 'I will show you the way to thresh, and separate the flesh from the bones.' 'O! will you so, young squire?' said John; 'I will show you the way to make naughty boys good.' He then left the barn, but presently returned accompanied by a gentleman, upon the sight of whom Will let fall the flail, which he was till then brandishing over Simon's head, and was going away, when the gentleman taking hold of his hand, said, 'You do not stir from this place, Master William, nor have one mouthful of breakfast, till you have asked the men pardon for your behaviour, and likewise sifted every grain of corn from the chaff which you have mixed with it. When you have done that, you may have some food, but not before; and afterward you may spend the rest of the day in threshing, then you will be a better judge, my boy, of the fatigue and labour of it, and find how you should like, after working hard all day, to have it rendered useless by a mischievous boy. Remember, William, what I have now said to you, for I do insist upon being minded; and I promise you, that if you offer to play, or do anything else today, you shall be punished very severely.' The gentleman then went away. Will muttered something, I could not exactly hear what, began to sift the corn, and so much had he mixed together, that he did not go in for his breakfast till after I had heard the church clock strike one, though it was before eight when he came into the barn. In about an hour he returned, and the other boy with him, who addressed him, saying, 'Ah! Will, you had better have taken my advice, and not have done so: I thought what you would get by your nice fun as you called it. I never knew any good come of mischief; it generally brings those who do it into disgrace; or if they should happen to escape unpunished, still it is always attended with some inconvenience: it is an ill-natured disposition which can take pleasure in giving trouble to any one.' 'Do hold your tongue, James,' replied Will; 'I declare I have not patience to hear you preach, you are so prodigiously wise, and prudent, and sober; you had better go indoors and sew with your mamma, for you talk just as if you were a girl, and not in the least like a boy of spirit.' 'Like a girl!' resumed James. 'Are girls then the only folk who have any sense, or good nature? Or what proof does it shew of spirit to be fond of mischief, and giving people trouble? It is like a monkey of spirit indeed; but I cannot say, that I see either spirit or sense in making the clean clothes fall into the dirt, or mixing the corn and chaff, for the sake of making the poor servants do them all over again: if these things are a sign of any spirit. I am sure it is of an evil one, and not at all such as I wish to possess, though I no more want to sit still, or work with a needle, than you do; but I hope there are other ways of showing my spirit, as you call it, than by doing mischief, and being ill-natured. I do not think my papa ever seems to be effeminate, or want sufficient spirit; but he would scorn to give unnecessary trouble to anybody: and so will Tom Vaulter, though no boy in the world loves play better than he does; he plays at cricket the best of any boy in the school, and I am sure none can beat him at tennis; and as for skipping, I never saw a boy skip so well in all my life; and I am sure he would beat you, with all your spirit, out and out twenty times, either at running, or sliding, or swimming, or climbing a tree. And yet he never gives trouble to anybody for the sake of fun; he is one of the best-tempered boys in the world; and whether it is like a girl or not, he always does what he knows to be right and kind; and if that is being like girls, why, with all my heart; I like girls well enough, and if they behave well I do not see why you should speak so contemptuously of them. My papa always says that he loves girls just as well as boys, and none but foolish and naughty boys despise and tease them.' Just as he said these words, Simon and John entered the barn, and seeing Will stand idle, 'Come, come, young gentleman,' said John, 'take up your flail and go to work, sir, to work! to work! night will be here presently, and you have done nothing yet.' Presently after the gentleman returned, and enforced John's advice for him to mind his work.

After Master Will had continued his employment some little time, he began to cry, saying, his arms ached ready to drop off, and his hand was so sore he could not bear it. 'Then doubtless,' replied his father, 'you would prodigiously like, after you have been labouring all day, to have your work to do over again, for the sake of diverting a foolish boy. But go on, William, I am determined that you shall, for one day, know what it is to work hard, and thereby be taught to pity, and help, not add to the fatigue of those who do.' The boy then went on with his business, though not without making great complaints, and shedding many tears. At length, however, evening came; and the gentleman, his son, and the two men, all went away, leaving Longtail and myself to enjoy our abundance. We passed another night in the sweetest undisturbed repose, and in the day had nothing to alarm our fears. In short, our situation was every way so perfectly happy and desirable, that we thought, although our mother had charged us not to return frequently to the same place, yet she could not

Dorothy Kilner

mean that we should not take up our abode in a spot so secure and comfortable. We therefore determined to continue where we were, till we should find some cause for removing. And happy had it been for us if we had kept to this resolution, and remained contented when we had everything requisite to make us so. Instead of which, after we had thus, free from care, passed our time about seven months, like fools as we were, we began to grow weary of our retirement, and of eating nothing but the same food; and agreed that we would again venture forth and seek for some other lodging, at the same time resolving, in case we could find no habitation that suited us, to return to the barn where we had enjoyed so many days of plenty and repose.

Accordingly, one fine moonlight Monday night, after securing our supper on the corn, we set forth, and travelled for some distance without any further molestation than our own natural fears created. At length we came to a brick house, with about five or six windows in front, and made our way into it through a small latticed window which gave air into the pantry; but on our arrival here we had no opportunity of so much as observing what it contained, for on our slipping down a cat instantly flew at us, and by the greatest good luck in the world, there chanced to be a hole in one of the boards of the floor close to the spot where we stood, into which we both were happy enough to pop, before she could catch us. Here we had time to reflect, and severely blame ourselves for not being satisfied with our state in the barn. 'When,' said I, addressing myself to my brother, 'when shall we grow wise, and learn to know that certain evil always attends every deviation from what is right. When we disobeyed the advice of our mother, and, tempted by cakes and other dainties, frequently returned to the same dangerous place, how severely did we suffer for it? And now, by our own discontent, and not being satisfied when so safely though more humbly lodged, into what trouble have we not plunged ourselves? How securely have we lived in the barn for the last seven months, and how happily might we still have continued there, had it not been for our restless dispositions? Ah! my brother, we have acted foolishly. We ought to have been contented when we were at peace, and should have considered that if we had not everything we could wish for, we had every thing that was necessary; and the life of a mouse was never designed for perfect happiness. Such enjoyment was never intended for our lot; it is the portion only of beings whose capacities are far superior to ours. We ought then to have been contented; and had we been so, we should have been as happy as our state of life would have admitted of.' 'What you say is certainly very true,' replied Longtail, 'and I sincerely wish that we had thought of these things before. But what must we now do? we said we would return to the barn in case of difficulties, but that is now impossible, as, if we attempt to retreat, the cat that drove us in here, will certainly destroy us; and yet in proceeding, what difficulties must we encounter, what dangers may we not run! Oh! my beloved Nimble,' continued he, 'what a life of hazard is ours! to what innumerable accidents are we hourly exposed! and how is every meal that we eat at the risk of our very existence!'

'It undoubtedly is,' replied I; 'but with all its troubles we still are very desirous of preserving it: let us not then, my brother, indulge our hearts with murmuring and finding fault with that life, which, notwithstanding all its evils, we value so highly. Rather let us

Dorothy Kilner

endeavour to learn experience, and, by conducting ourselves better, escape many of those troubles which we now suffer.' So saving, I advised him to follow me: 'for,' added I, 'it is impossible for us to exist in the spot in which we are at present; we must therefore strive to work our way into some other house or apartment, where we can at least find some food.' To this Longtail agreed; the rest of the night, and all the next day, we spent in nibbling and finding our way into a closet in the house, which richly repaid us for all our toil, as it contained sugar-plums, rice, millet, various kinds of sweetmeats, and what we liked better than all the rest, a paper of nice macaroons. On these we feasted most deliciously till our hunger was fully satisfied, and then creeping into a little hole, just big enough to contain us both, behind one of the jars of sweetmeats, reposed ourselves with a nap, after our various and great fatigues which we had gone through. I never was a remarkably sound sleeper, the least noise disturbs me, and I was awakened in the morning by the servant-maid's coming into the room to sweep it, and get it ready for the reception of her mistress and family, who soon after entered. As I wanted to know from whom the voices I heard proceeded, I stepped softly from behind the jar and just peeped under the door into the room, where I discovered a gentleman, two ladies, and a little boy and girl.

As I was totally unacquainted with all places of retreat, and did not know how soon any of them might have occasion to open the closet door, I instantly returned to my brother; and, awaking him, told him it was time for us to be upon our guard, as the family were all up and about.

Whilst we were thus situated, the first words I heard

distinctly were those of the gentleman, saying, 'No, Frank, I can never have a good opinion of him; the boy who could once deceive may, for aught I know, do so again; he has, by breaking his word, forfeited the only dependence one could possibly have in him. A person who has once lost his honour has no means left of gaining credit to his assertions. By honour, Frank, I would be understood to speak of veracity, of virtue, of scorning to commit a mean action, and not that brutish sense in which some understand it, as if it consisted in a readiness to fight and resent an injury; for so far am I from considering such behaviour as any proof of honour, that, on the contrary, I look upon it as a sure sign of want of proper spirit and true honour. Fools, bullies, and even cowards, will fight; whereas none but men of sense and resolution and true magnanimity know how to pardon and despise an insult.' 'But, indeed, sir,' replied the boy, 'at school, if one did not fight, they would laugh at one so, there would be no such thing as bearing it.' 'And for that very reason it is, my dear, that I say, to pass by and pardon an insult requires more resolution and courage than mere fighting does. When I wish you to avoid quarrelling and fighting, I by no means want you to become a coward, for I as much abhor a dastardly spirit as any boy in your school can possibly do; but I would wish you to convince them that you merited not that appellation, by showing through the whole of your behaviour, a resolution that despised accidental pain, and avoided revenging an affront for no other reason than because you were convinced it shewed a much nobler spirit to pardon than to resent. And you may be assured, my dear, few are the days that pass without affording us some opportunity of exerting our patience, and showing that, although we disdain quarrelling, still we are far from being cowards.

'I remember, when I was at school, there was one boy, who, from his first coming, declined upon all occasions engaging in any battle; he even gave up many of his just rights to avoid quarrelling, which conduct, instead of gaining (as it justly deserved) the approbation of his companions, drew upon him the insult and abuse of the whole school; and they were perpetually teasing him with the opprobrious title of coward. For some time he bore it with great good-humour, and endeavoured to laugh it off; but, finding that had no effect, he one day thus addressed us: - "If you suppose that I like to be called a coward, you are all very much mistaken; or if you think me one, I assure you that you are not less so; for no boy in the school should, if put to the trial, show greater resolution than myself. Indeed, I think it no small proof of patience that I have borne your repeated insults so long; when I could, by behaving more like a savage beast, and less like a reasonable creature, have established my character at once; but I abhor quarrelling, my soul detests to treat my fellow-creatures as if they were brutes, from whose fangs I must defend myself; but if nothing else but fighting will convince you that I possess not less courage than yourselves, I will now offer, in cold blood, to engage with the biggest boy in the school. If I conquer him, it will be a sign that I know how to defend myself; and if he conquers me, I will, by my behaviour, give a proof that I am not wanting in resolution to suffer pain, although I never will so far demean the character of a reasonable creature and a Christian, as to fight upon every trifling disagreement or insult." No sooner had he uttered these words, than every boy present was loud either in his commendation or condemnation. One quarter of them, convinced of the justness of his arguments, highly extolled his forbearance; whilst the other three parts, with still greater noise, only called him a bully and a mean-spirited coward, who dared not fight, and for that reason made such a fine speech, hoping to intimidate them. "Well then," said he, "if such is your opinion, why will none of you accept my offer? you surely cannot be afraid, you who are such brave fellows, of such true courage, and such noble spirits, cannot be afraid of a coward and a bully! Why, therefore, does not one of you step forward, and put my fine speech to the test? Otherwise, after I have thus challenged you all, I hope none for the future will think they have any right to call me coward; though I again declare my fixed resolution against fighting."

'Just as he said this, a voice calling for help, was heard from a lane adjoining to the play-yard. Immediately we all flocked to the side nearest whence it proceeded; and, clambering upon benches, watering-pots, or whatever came first in our way, peeped over the wall, where we discovered two well-grown lads, about seventeen or eighteen, stripping a little boy of his clothes, and beating him for his outcries in a most cruel manner; and at a little distance farther down the lane, sat a company of gypsies, to whom the two lads evidently belonged. At the sight of this we were all much distressed, and wished to relieve the boy; though, discovering so large a party, we were too much afraid to venture, till Tomkins (the boy I before spoke about) instantly jumped from the wall, and only saying, "Has nobody courage to follow me?" ran toward them as fast as possible, and with uncommon strength and agility placed himself between them and the boy, and began defending himself in the best manner he could; which he did for some time with great dexterity, none of his fighting schoolfellows having courage to go to his assistance. At length, however, seeing it impossible for him to stand out any longer against two so much stronger than himself, the boys agreed to secure themselves by numbers, and to sally forth to his assistance altogether. This scheme succeeded, and very shortly rescued Tomkins from his antagonists. He thanked them for their assistance, saying, at the same time, "I hope you will no longer doubt my courage, or my abilities to fight, when it is necessary or in a good cause." After so signal a proof of his viler, his greatest enemies could no longer doubt it; and, without ever engaging in foolish battles, he passed through school as much respected as any boy, and his magnanimity was never again called in question.'

As the gentleman stopped speaking, the little girl called out, 'O, papa, the coach is at the door.' 'Is it, my dear?' returned the father. 'Well then, stop, my love,' said one of the ladies, 'I have got a few cakes for you: stay, and take them before you go.' She then unlocked the closet where we were, and took down the paper of macaroons, among which we had so comfortably regaled ourselves; when, observing the hole in the paper through which we entered, 'O dear!' she exclaimed, 'the mice have actually got into my cupboard. I will move all the things out this very morning, and lock the cat up in it; for I shall be undone if the mice once get footing here; they will soon spoil all my stores, and that will never do.' She then kissed both the children; and, giving them the cakes, they, the gentleman, and another lady, all departed; and she instantly began to move the boxes and jars from the closet; whilst we, terrified almost out of our wits, sat trembling behind one of them, not daring to stir, yet dreading the cat's approach every moment.

We were soon, however, obliged to move our quarters, for the lady taking down the very jar which concealed us, we were forced (without knowing where we were) to jump down instantly. In vain we sought all round the room for some avenue whereat we might escape; the apartment was too well fitted up to admit the smallest crack; and we must then certainly have been destroyed, had we not, with uncommon presence of mind, ran up the back of the lady's gown, by which means she lost sight of us, and gave us an opportunity to make our escape, as she opened the door to order the cat to be brought in. We seized the lucky moment, and, dropping from her gown, fled with the utmost haste out at the house door, which happened to be wide open; and I, without once looking behind me, ran on till I discovered a little crack in the brick wall, which I entered, and which, after many turnings and windings, brought me to this house, where I have now continued skulking about in its different apartments for above a month; during which time I have not heard the least tidings of my beloved brother Longtail. Whether, therefore, any mischief befell him as he followed me, or whether he entered the crack with me and then lost sight of me, I know not; but in vain have I sought him every day since my arrival within these walls, and so anxious am I to learn what is become of him, that I am now come forth, contrary to my nature, to engage your compassion, and to beseech you, in case -

At this moment, the door of my room opened, and my servant coming hastily in, the mouse jumped from my table, and precipitately retreated to the same hole from whence it first addressed me; and though I have several times peeped into it, and even laid little bits of cake to entice it back again, yet have I never been able to see it any where since. Should either that, or any other, ever

Dorothy Kilner

again favour me so far with their confidence, as to instruct me with their history, I will certainly communicate it with all possible speed to my little readers; who I hope have been wise enough to attend to the advice given them in the preceding pages, although it was delivered to them by one as insignificant as a MOUSE.

PART II.

INTRODUCTION

It is now some months ago since I took leave of my little readers, promising, in case I should ever hear any further tidings of either Nimble or Longtail, I would certainly communicate it to them; and, as I think it extremely wrong not to fulfil any engagement we enter into, I look upon myself bound to give them all the information I have since gained, relating to those two little animals; and I doubt not but they will be glad to hear what happened to them, after Nimble was frightened from my writing table by the entrance of my servant. If I recollect right, I have already told you, that I frequently peeped into the hole in the skirting-board, and laid bits of cake to try to entice my little companion back, but all to no purpose: and I had quite given over all hopes of ever again seeing him, when one day, as I was putting my hand into a large jar, which had some Turkey figs in it, I felt something soft at the bottom, and taking it out, found it to be a poor little mouse, not quite dead, but so starved and weak, that upon my placing it upon the table, it had not strength sufficient to get from me. A little boy happened to be standing by me, who, upon the sight of the mouse, began to beg me to give it to the cat, or kill it, 'for I don't like mice,' said he; 'pray, ma'am, put it away.' 'Not like mice,' replied I; 'what can be your objection to such a little soft creature as this?' and taking advantage of its weakness, I picked it up, and held it in the palm of one hand, whilst I stroked it with the fingers of my right. 'Poor little mouse,' said I, 'who can be afraid of such a little object as this? Do you not feel ashamed of yourself, Joe, to fear such a little creature as this? Only look at it, observe how small it is, and then consider your own size, and surely, my dear, you will blush to think of being no more of a man than to fear a mouse! Look at me, Joe,' continued I, 'see, I will kiss it, I am not at all afraid that it will hurt me.' When, lifting it up toward my face, I heard it say, in the faintest voice possible, 'Do you not know me?' I instantly recollected my little friend Nimble, and rejoiced at so unexpectedly finding him. 'What, is it you, little Nimble,' exclaimed I, 'that I again behold? Believe me, I am heartily rejoiced once more to find you; but tell me, where have you been, what have you done, whom have you seen, and what have you learned since you last left me?' 'Oh!' replied he, in a voice so low I could scarcely hear him, 'I have seen many things; but I am so faint and weak for want of food and fresh air, that I doubt I shall never live to tell you; but, for pity's sake have compassion on me, either put me out of my present misery by instantly killing me, or else give me something to eat; for, if you knew my sufferings, I am sure it would grieve your heart.' 'Kill you!' returned I, 'no, that I will not: on the contrary, I will try by every method to restore you to health, and all the happiness a mouse is capable of feeling.' I then instantly sent for some bread, and had the satisfaction of seeing him eat very heartily of it, after which he seemed much refreshed, and began to move about a little more suitable to his name; for, in truth, when I first found him, no living creature in the world could appear less deserving of the appellation of Nimble. I then fetched him a little milk, and gave him a lump of sugar to nibble; after eating of which he begged to retire into some safe little hole to take a nap, from whence he promised to return as soon as he should wake; and accordingly, in about an hour he again appeared on my table, and began as follows.

I was frightened away from you just as I was going to implore your compassion for any unfortunate mouse that might happen to fall within your power; lest you should destroy my dear and only surviving brother, Longtail; but somebody entering the room, prevented me, and after I had regained my hiding place, I resolved to quit the house, and once more set out in search of my beloved brother. Accordingly, with great difficulty I made my way out of the house; but my distress was much increased upon finding the snow so deep upon the ground, that it was impossible for me to attempt to stir, as upon stepping one foot out to try, I found it far too deep for me to fathom the bottom. This greatly distressed me. 'Alas!' said I to myself, 'what shall I do now? To proceed is impossible; and to return is very melancholy, without any tidings of my dear, dear Longtail.' But I was interrupted in the midst of these reflections, by the appearance of two cats, who came running with such violence as to pass by without observing me: however, it put me in such consternation, that regardless where I went, I sprung forward, and sunk so deep in the snow that I must inevitably soon have perished, had not a boy come to the very place where I was, to gather snow for making snowballs to throw at his companions. Happily for me, he took me up in his hand, in the midst of the snow, which not less alarmed me, when I considered the sufferings I had before endured, and the cruel death of my brother Brighteyes, from the hands of boys. Oh!

Dorothy Kilner

thought I to myself, what new tortures shall I now experience? Better had I perished in the cold snow, than be spared only to be tormented by the cruel hands of unthinking children.

Scarcely had I made this reflection, when the boy called out, upon seeing me move, 'Lud! what have I got here?' at the same instant tossing the handful of snow from him in a violent hurry, without attempting to press it into a ball. Over I turned head and heels, wondering what further would be my fate, when I was happy to find I fell unhurt upon some hay, which was laid in the yard to fodder the cows and horses. Here I lay some time, so frightened by my adventure, as to be unable to move, and my little heart beat as if it would have burst its way through my breast; nor were my apprehensions at all diminished by the approach of a man, who gathered the hay up in his arms, and carried it (with me in the midst of it) into the stable; where, after littering down the horses, he left me once more to my own reflections.

After he had been gone some time, and all things were quiet, I began to look about me, and soon found my way into a corn bin, where I made a most delicious supper, and slept free from any disturbance till the morning, when fearing I might be discovered, in case he should want any of the oats for his horses, I returned by the same place I had entered, and hid myself in one corner of the hayloft, where I passed the whole of the day more free from alarm than often falls to the lot of any of my species, and in the evening again returned to regale myself with corn, as I had done the night before. The great abundance with which I was surrounded, strongly tempted me to continue where I was; but then the thoughts of my absent brother embittered all my peace, and the advice of my mother came so much across my mind, that I determined before the next morning I would again venture forth and seek my fortune and my brother. Accordingly, after having eaten a very hearty meal, I left the bin, and was attempting to get out of the stable, when one of the horses being taken suddenly ill, made so much noise with his kicking and struggling, as to alarm the family, and the coachman entering with a lantern in his hand, put me into such consternation, that I ran for shelter into the pocket of a great coat, which hung up upon a peg next the harness of the horses. Here I lay snug for some hours, not daring to stir, as I smelt the footsteps of a cat frequently pass by, and heard the coachman extol her good qualities to a man who accompanied him into the stable; saying she was the best mouser in the kingdom. 'I do not believe,' added he, 'I have a mouse in the stable or loft, she keeps so good a lookout. For the last two days I lent her to the cook, to put into her pantry, but I have got her back again, and I would not part with her for a crown; no, not for the best silver crown that ever was coined in the Tower.' Then, through a little moth hole in the lining of the coat, I saw him lift her up, stroke her, and put her upon the back of one of the horses, where she stretched herself out, and went to sleep.

In this situation I did not dare to stir, I had too often seen how eager cats are to watch mice, to venture out of the pocket, whilst she was so near me, especially as I did not at all know the holes or cracks round the stable, and should, therefore, had she jumped down, been quite at a loss where to run. So I determined to continue where I was till either hunger forced me, or the absence of the cat gave a better opportunity of escaping. But scarce had I taken up this resolution when the coachman again entered, and suddenly taking the coat from the peg, put it on, and marched out with me in his pocket.

It is utterly impossible to describe my fear and consternation at this event, to jump out whilst in the stable exposed me to the jaws of the cat, and to attempt it when out of doors was but again subjecting myself to be frozen to death, for the snow continued still on the ground; yet to stay in his pocket was running the chance of suffering a still more dreadful death by the barbarous hands of man; and nothing did I expect, in case he should find me, but either to be tortured like Softdown, or given to be the sport of his favorite cat - a fate almost as much dreaded as the other. However it was soon put out of my power to determine, for whilst I was debating in my own mind what course I had better take, he mounted the coachbox, and drove away with me in his pocket, till he came to a large house, about a mile distant from this place; there he put down the company he had in the coach, and then drove into the yard. But he had not been there many moments before the coachman of the family he was come to, invited him into the kitchen to warm himself, drink a mug of ale, and eat a mouthful of cold meat. As soon as he entered, and had paid the proper compliments to the Mrs. Betties and Mollies at the place, he pulled off his great coat, and hung it across the back of his chair. I instantly seized the first opportunity and whilst they were all busy assembling round the luncheon table, made my escape, and ran under a cupboard door close to the chimney, where I had an opportunity of seeing and hearing all that passed, part of which conversation I will relate to you.

'Well, Mr. John,' said a footman, addressing himself to

the man whose pocket I had just left, 'how fare you? Are you pretty hearty? You look well, I am sure.' 'Aye, and so I am, replied he. 'I never was better in all my life; I live comfortably, have a good master and mistress, eat and drink bravely, and what can a man wish for more? For my part I am quite contented, and if I do but continue to enjoy my health, I am sure I shall be very ungrateful not to be so.' 'That's true,' said the other, 'but the misfortune of it is, people never know when they are well off, but are apt to fret and wish and wish and fret, for something or other all their lives, and so never have any enjoyment. Now for my own part, I must needs confess, that I cannot help wishing I was a gentleman, and think I should be a deal happier if I was.' 'Pshaw!' replied John, 'I don't like now to hear a man say so; it looks as if you are discontented with the state in which you are placed, and depend upon it, you are in the one that is fittest for you, or you would not have been put into it. And as for being happier if you were a gentleman, I don't know what to say to it. To be sure, to have a little more money in one's pocket, nobody can deny that it would be very agreeable; and to be at liberty to come in and go out when one pleased, to be sure would be very comfortable. But still, Bob, still you may assure yourself, that no state in this world is free from care, and if we were turned into lords, we should find many causes for uneasiness. So here's your good health,' said he, lifting the mug to his mouth, 'wishing, my lad, you may be contented, cheerful, and good humoured; for without these three requisites, content, cheerfulness, and good humour, no one person upon earth, rich or poor, old or young, can ever feel comfortable or happy; and so here's to you, I say.' 'And here's the same good wishes to you,' said a clean decent cook-woman servant, who took up the mug upon John's putting it down. 'Content, cheerfulness, and good humour, I think was the toast.' Then wiping her mouth, as she began her speech, she added, 'and an excellent one it is: I wish all folks would mind it, and endeavour to acquire three such good qualifications.' 'I am sure,' rejoined another female servant, whose name I heard was Sally, 'I wish so too: at least I wish Miss Mary would try to gain a little more of the good humour; for I never came near such a cross crab in my life as it is. I declare I hate the sight of the girl, she is such a proud little minx she would not vouchsafe to speak to a poor servant for the world; as if she thought because we are poorer, we were therefore not of the same nature: her sisters, I think are worth ten of her, they always reply so civilly if a body speaks to them, and say, "Yes, if you please, Mrs. "Sally, or "No, thank you, Mr. Bob;" or "I should be obliged to you if you would do so and so, Mrs. Nelly," and not plain yes or no, as she does; and well too if you can get even that from her; for sometimes I declare she will not deign to give one any answer at all.' 'Aye, that is a sure thing she won't,' replied the maid servant who first drank, 'it is a sad thing she should behave so; I can't think, for my part, where she learns it; I am sure neither her papa nor mamma set her the example of it, for they always speak as pretty and as kind as it is possible to do; and I have heard, with my own ears, my mistress tell her of it twenty and twenty times, but she will do so. I am sure it is a sad thing that she should, for she will always make people dislike her. I am sure, if young gentlemen and ladies did not know how it makes people love them to speak civilly and kind, they would take great care not to behave like Miss Mary. Do you know, the other day, when Mrs. Lime's maid brought little Miss Peggy to see my mistress, when she went away, she made a courtesy to Miss Mary, and said,

"Good morning to you, Miss." And would you think it, the child stood like a stake, and never returned it so much as by a nod of the head, nor did she open her lips. I saw by her looks the maid took notice of it, and I am sure I have such a regard for the family, that I felt quite ashamed of her behaviour.' 'Oh! she served me worse than that,' resumed Sally, 'for, would you believe it, the other day I begged her to be so kind as to let her mamma know I wanted to speak with her; and I did not choose to go into the room myself, because I was dirty, and there was company there; but for all I desired her over and over only just to step in (and she was at play close to the door) yet, could you suppose it possible, she was ill-natured enough to refuse me, and would not do it at last.' 'Well, if ever I heard the like of that!' exclaimed John, whose pocket I had been in. 'I think that was being cross indeed, and if a child of mine was to behave in that surly manner, I would whip it to death almost. I abominate such unkind doings, let everyone, I say, do as they like to be done by, and that is the only way to be happy, and the only way to deserve to be so; for if folks will not try to be kind, and oblige others, why should anybody try to please them? And if Miss Mary was my girl, and chose to behave rude and cross to the servants, if I was her papa, I would order them to refuse doing anything for her. I would soon humble her pride I warrant you, for nobody should make her puddings, or cut her bread, or do anything for her till she learned to be kind, and civil, and thankful too, for all that was done for her. I have no notion, for my part, for a child to give herself such airs for nothing; and because her parents happen to have a little more money in their pockets, for that reason to think she may be rude to poor folks; but though servants are poor, still surely they are richer than she is; I should like to ask her how much she has got? and which way she came by it? A child I am sure is no richer than a beggar, for they have not a farthing that is not given them through mere bounty; whereas a servant who works for his living, has a right and just claim to his wages, and may truly call them his own; but a child has not one farthing that is not its parents. So here's my service to you, Miss,' said he, (again lifting the ale-mug to his mouth) 'and wishing her a speedy reformation of manners, I drink to her very good health.'

John drank to the bottom of the mug, and then shaking the last drop into the ashes under the grate, he told the following story, as he sat swinging the mug by its handle across his two forefingers, which he had joined for that purpose.

'When my father was a young man he lived at one Mr. Speedgo's, as upper footman: they were vastly rich. Mr. Speedgo was a merchant, and by good luck he gathered gold as fast as his neighbours would pick up stones (as a body may say). So they kept two or three carriages, there was a coach, and a chariot, and a phaeton, and I can't tell what besides, and a power of servants you may well suppose to attend them all; and very well they lived, with plenty of victuals and drink. But though they wanted for nothing still they never much loved either their master or mistress, they used to give their orders in so haughty and imperious a manner; and if asked a civil question, answer so shortly, as if they thought their servants not worthy of their notice: so that, in short, no one loved them, nor their children either, for they brought them up just like themselves, to despise everyone poorer than they were; and to speak as cross to their servants as if they had been so many adders they were afraid would bite them.

'I have heard my father say, that if Master Speedgo wanted his horse to be got ready, he would say, "Saddle my horse!" in such a displeasing manner as made it quite a burthen to do anything for him. Or if the young ladies wanted a piece of bread and butter, or cake, they would say, "Give me a bit of cake;" or, if they added the word pray to it, they spoke in such a grumpy way, as plainly showed they thought themselves a deal better than their servants; forgetting that an honest servant is just as worthy a member of society as his master, and whilst he behaves well, as much deserving of civility as anybody. But to go on with my story. I have already told you Mr. Speedgo was very rich and very proud, nor would he on any account suffer anyone to visit at his house whom he thought below him, as he called it; or at least, if he did, he always took care to behave to them in such a manner, as plainly to let them know he thought he showed a mighty favour in conversing with them.

'Among the rest of the servants there was one Molly Mount, as good a hearted girl, my father says, as ever lived: she had never received much education, because her parents could not afford to give her any, and she learned to read after she was at Mr. Speedgo's from one of the housemaids, who was kind enough to teach her a little; but you may suppose, from such sort of teaching, she was no very good scholar. However, she read well enough to be able to make out some chapters in the Bible; and an excellent use she made of them, carefully fulfilling every duty she there found recommended as necessary for a Christian to practice. She used often to say she was perfectly contented in her station, and only wished for more money that she might have it in her power to do more good. And sometimes, when she was dressing and attending the young ladies of the family, she would advise them to behave prettier than they did; telling them, "That by kindness and civility they would be so far from losing respect, that, on the contrary, they would much gain it. For we cannot (she would very truly say) have any respect for those people who seem to forget their human nature, and behave as if they thought themselves superior to the rest of their fellow-creatures. Young ladies and gentlemen have no occasion to make themselves very intimate or familiar with their servants; but everybody ought to speak civilly and good-humouredly, let it be to whom it may: and if I was a lady I should make it a point never to look cross or speak gruffly to the poor, for fear they should think I forgot I was of the same human nature as they were." By these kind of hints, which every now and then she would give to the misses, they were prodigiously offended, and complained of her insolence, as they called it, to their mamma, who very wrongly, instead of teaching them to behave better, joined with them in blaming Molly for her freedom, and, to show her displeasure at her conduct, put on a still haughtier air, whenever she spoke to her, than she did to any other of the servants. Molly, however, continued to behave extremely well, and often very seriously lamented in the kitchen the wrong behaviour of the family. "I don't mind it," she would say, "for my own part; I know that I do my duty, and their cross looks and proud behaviour can do me no real harm: but I cannot help grieving for their sakes; it distresses me to think that people who ought to know better, should, by their ill conduct, make themselves so many enemies, when they could so easily gain friends - I am astonished how anybody can act so foolishly."

'In this sensible manner she would frequently talk

about the sin as well as the folly of pride. And one day, as she was talking to her fellow-servants, rather louder than in prudence she ought to have done, her two young ladies overheard her; and the next time she went to dress them, they enquired what it was she had been saying to the other maids. "Indeed, ladies," said she, "I hope you will excuse my telling you. I think, if you give yourselves time to reflect a little, you will not insist upon knowing, as it is beneath such rich ladies as you are, to concern yourselves with what poor servants talk about." This answer did not, however, satisfy them, and they positively commanded her to let them know. Molly was by far too good a woman to attempt to deceive anyone; she therefore replied, "If, ladies, you insist upon knowing what I said, I hope you will not take anything amiss that I may tell you, thus compelled as I am by your commands. You must know then, Miss Betsy and Miss Rachael, that I was saying how sad a thing it was for people to be proud because they are rich; or to fancy, because they happen to have a little more money, that for that reason they are better than their servants, when in reality the whole that makes one person better than another is, having superior virtues, being kinder and more good natured, and readier to assist and serve their fellow-creatures; these are the qualifications, I was saying, that make people beloved, and not being possessed of money. Money may, indeed, procure servants to do their business for them, but it is not in the power of all the riches in the world to purchase the love and esteem of anyone. What a sad thing then it is, when gentlefolks behave so as to make themselves despised; and that will ever be the case with all those who, like (excuse me, ladies, you insisted upon my telling you what I said) Miss Betsy, and Miss Rachael, and Master James, show such contempt to all their inferiors. Nobody could wish children of their fortunes to make themselves too free, or play with their servants; but if they were little kings and queens, still they ought to speak kind and civil to everyone. Indeed our king and queen would scorn to behave like the children of this family, and if - " She was going on, but they stopped her, saying, "If you say another word, we will push you out of the room this moment, you rude, bold, insolent woman; you ought to be ashamed of speaking so disrespectfully of your betters; but we will tell our mamma, that we will, and she won't suffer you to allow your tongue such liberties." "If," replied Molly, "I have offended you, I am sorry for it, and beg your pardon, ladies; I am sure I had no wish to do so; and you should remember that you both insisted upon my telling you what I had been saying." "So we did," said they, "but you had no business to say it all; and I promise you my mamma shall know it."

'In this manner they went on for some time; but, to make short of my story, they represented the matter in such a manner to their mother, that she dismissed Molly from her service, with a strict charge never to visit the house again. "For," said Mrs. Speedgo, "no servant who behaves as you have done, shall ever enter my doors again, or eat another mouthful in my house." Molly had no desire so suddenly to quit her place; but as her conscience perfectly acquitted her of any wilful crime, after receiving her wages, respectfully wishing all the family their health, and taking a friendly leave of her fellow-servants, she left the house, and soon engaged herself as dairy-maid in a farmer's family, about three miles off; in which place she behaved so extremely well, and so much to the satisfaction of her master and mistress, that, after she had lived there a little more than two years, with their entire approbation, she was married to their eldest son, a sober, worthy young man, to whom his father gave a fortune not much less than three thousand pounds, with which he bought and stocked a very pretty farm in Somersetshire, where they lived as happy as virtue and affluence could make them. By industry and care they prospered beyond their utmost expectations, and, by their prudence and good behaviour, gained the esteem and love of all who knew them.

'To their servants (for they soon acquired riches enough to keep three or four, I mean household ones, besides the number that were employed in the farming business) they behaved with such kindness and civility, that had they even given less wages than their neighbours, they would never have been in want of any; everyone being desirous of getting into a family where they were treated with such kindness and condescension.

'In this happy manner they continued to live for many years, bringing up a large family of children to imitate their virtues; but one great mortification they were obliged to submit to, which was that of putting their children very early to boarding school, a circumstance which the want of education in Mrs. and indeed I may add Mr. Flail, rendered absolutely necessary.

'But I am afraid, Mrs. Sally and Mrs. Nelly, you will be tired, as I have but half told my story; but I will endeavour to make short work of it, though indeed it deserves to be noticed, for it will teach one a great deal, and convince one how little the world's riches are to be depended on.

'I have said, you know, that Mr. Speedgo was a

merchant, and a very rich one too. It is unknown what vast sums of money he used to spend! when, would you think it, either through spending it too fast, or some losses he met with in trade, he broke all to nothing, and had not a farthing to pay his creditors. I forgot how many thousand pounds it was he owed; but it was a vast great many. Well! this you may be sure was a great mortification to them; they begged for mercy from their creditors; but as in their prosperity they had never shown much mercy themselves to those they thought beneath them, so now they met with very little from others: the poor saying they deserved it for their pride; the rich condemning them for their presumption, in trying to vie with those of superior birth; and those who had been less successful in business, blaming them for their extravagance, which, they said, had justly brought on them their misfortunes.

'In this distress, in vain it was they applied for assistance to those they had esteemed their friends; for as they never had been careful to form their connections with people of real merit, only seeking to be acquainted with those who were rich and prosperous, so now they could no longer return their civilities, they found none were ready to show them any, but everyone seemed anxious to keep from them as much as possible. Thus distressed, and finding no one willing to help them, the young squire, Master James, was obliged to go to sea: while Miss Betsy and Miss Rachael were even forced to try to get their living by service, a way of life they were both ill qualified to undertake, for they had always so accustomed themselves to be waited on and attended, that they scarcely knew how to help themselves, much less how to work for others. The consequence of which was, they gave so little satisfaction to their employers, that they staid but a little time in a place, and from so frequently changing, no family, who wished to be well settled, would admit them, as they thought it impossible they could be good servants whom no one thought worthy of keeping.

'It is impossible to describe the many and great mortifications those two young ladies met with. They now frequently recollected the words of Molly Mount, and earnestly wished they had attended to them whilst it was in their power, as by so doing they would have secured to themselves friends. And they very forcibly found, that, although they were poor and servants, yet they were as sensible of kind treatment and civility, as if they had been richer.

'After they had been for some years changing from place to place, always obliged to put up with very low wages, upon account of their being so ill qualified for servants, it happened that Miss Betsy got into service at Watchet, a place about three miles distant from Mr. Flail's farm. Here she had a violent fit of illness, and not having been long enough in the family to engage their generosity to keep her, she was dismissed upon account of her ill health rendering her wholly incapable of doing her business for which she was hired. She then, with the very little money she had, procured a lodging in a miserable little dirty cottage; but through weakness being unable to work, she soon exhausted her whole stock, and was even obliged to quit this habitation, bad as it was, and for some days support herself wholly by begging from door to door, often meeting with very unkind language for so idle an employment; some people telling her to go to her parish, when, alas! her parish was many miles distant, and she, poor creature, had no means of getting there.

'At last she wandered, in this distressful situation, to the house of Mr. Flail, and walked into the farm yard just at the time the cows were being milked. She, who for a long time had tasted nothing but bits of broken bread, and had no drink besides water she had scooped up in her hands, looked at the quantity of fresh milk with a most wishful eye; and, going to the women who were milking, she besought them in a moving manner to give her a draught, as she was almost ready to perish. "For pity's sake," said she, "have compassion upon a poor wretch, dying with sickness, hunger, and thirst; it is a long time since I have tasted a mouthful of wholesome victuals, my lips are now almost parched with thirst, and I am so faint for want, that I can scarcely stand; my sufferings are very great indeed, it would melt a heart of stone to hear the story of my woes. Oh! have pity upon a fellow-creature then, and give me one draught of that milk, which can never be missed out of so vast a quantity as you have there, and may you never, never, know what it is to suffer as I now do." To this piteous request, she received for answer, the common one of "Go about your business, we have nothing for you, so don't come here." "We should have enough to do indeed," said one of the milkers, "if we were to give every idle beggar who would like a draught of this delicious milk; but no, indeed, we shall not give you a drop; so go about your business, and don't come plaguing us here." Mrs. Flail, who happened to be in the yard, with one of her children who was feeding the chickens, overheard enough of this to make her come forward, and enquire what was the matter. "Nothing, ma"am," replied the milk-maid, "only I was sending away this nasty dirty creature, who was so bold as to come asking for milk indeed! But beggars grow so impudent now-a-days there never was the like of it." "Oh fie!" returned Mrs.

Flail, shocked at her inhuman way of speaking, "fie upon you, to speak in so unkind a manner of a poor creature in distress." Then turning to the beggar, she inquired what she wanted, in so mild a tone of voice, that it encouraged her to speak and tell her distress.

'Mrs. Flail listened with the greatest attention, and could not help being struck with her speech and appearance; for though she was clothed in rags (having parted with all her better clothes to pay for lodging and food) still there was a something in her language and manner which discovered that she was no common beggar. Betsy had stood all the time with her eyes fixed upon the ground, scarcely once lifting them to look at the face of Mrs. Flail; and she was so changed herself by her troubles and sickness, that it was impossible for any one who had ever seen Miss Speedgo, to recollect her in her present miserable state. Mrs. Flail, however, wanted no farther inducement to relieve her than to hear she was in want. "Every fellow-creature in distress," she used to say, "was a proper object of her bounty; and whilst she was blessed with plenty she thought it her duty to relieve, as far as she prudently could, all whom she knew to be in need." She therefore fetched a mug, and, filling it with milk herself, gave it to the poor woman to drink. "Here," said she, "take this, good woman, and I hope it will refresh and be of service to you." Betsy held out her hand for it, and, lifting her eyes up to look at Mrs. Flail, whilst she thanked her for her kindness, was greatly astonished to discover in her benefactress, the features of her old servant, Molly Mount. "Bless me!" said she, with an air of confusion, "What do I see? Who is it? Where am I? Madam, pardon my boldness, but pray forgive me, ma"am, but is not your name Mount?" "It was," replied Mrs. Flail, "but I have been married for thirteen years to a Mr. Flail, and that is my name now. But, pray, where did you ever see me before? or how came you to know anything of me?" Poor Betsy could return no answer, her shame at being seen by her servant that was, in her present condition, and the consciousness of having so ill-treated that very servant, to whose kindness she was now indebted; all together were too much for her in her weak state, and she fell senseless at Mrs. Flail's feet.

'This still added to Mrs. Flail's surprise, and she had her carried into the house and laid upon a bed, where she used every means to bring her to herself again; which, after a considerable time, succeeded; and she then (covered with shame and remorse) told her who she was, and how she came into that miserable condition. No words can describe the astonishment Mrs. Flail was in, at hearing the melancholy story of her sufferings; nor is it possible to tell with what generosity and kindness she strove to comfort her, telling her to compose herself, for she should no longer be in want of any thing. "I have, thank Heaven," said she, "a most worthy good man for my husband, who will rejoice with me in having it in his power to relieve a suffering fellow-creature. Do not, therefore, any longer distress yourself upon what passed between us formerly. I had, for my part, forgotten it, if you had not now told it me; but, however I might then take the liberty to censure you for too much haughtiness. I am sure I have no occasion to do so now. Think no more, therefore, I beseech you, upon those times which are now past; but be comforted, and make yourself as happy as in my humble plain manner of living you can possibly do."

'She then furnished her with some of her own clothes,

till she could procure her new ones, and sent immediately for a physician from the next town; by following of whose prescription, together with good nursing, and plenty of all necessaries, she soon recovered her health; but she was too deeply affected with the thoughts of her former misconduct ever to feel happy in her situation, though Mrs. Flail used every method in her power to render her as comfortable as possible. Nor did she confine her goodness only to this one daughter, but sent also for her sister and mother (her father being dead), and fitted up a neat little house for them near their own. But as the Flails could not afford wholly to maintain them for nothing, they entrusted the poultry to their care; which enabled them to do with one servant less; and by that means they could, without any great expense, afford to give them sufficient to make their lives comfortable, that is, as far as their own reflections would let them; for the last words Mrs. Speedgo said to Molly, when she parted from her, dwelt continually upon her mind, and filled her with shame and remorse.

"'I told her," said she, "that she should never again come into my doors, or eat another mouthful in my house; and now it is her bounty alone which keeps us all from perishing. Oh! how unworthy are we of such goodness! True, indeed, was what she told you, that kindness and virtue were far more valuable than riches. Goodness and kindness no time or change can take from us; but riches soon fly as it were away, and then what are we the better for having been once possessed of them?'"

Here Mr. John stopped, and jumping hastily up, and turning round to Mrs. Sally, Mrs. Nelly, and Mr. Bob, exclaimed, rubbing his hands - 'There ladies, I have finished my story; and, let me tell you, so long preaching has made my throat dry, so another mug of ale, if you please, Master Bobby (tapping him at the same time upon the shoulder), another mug of ale, my boy; for faith, talking at the rate I have done, is enough to wear a man's lungs out, and, in truth, I have need of something to hearten me after such fatigue.'

'Well, I am sure,' replied Mrs. Sally and Mrs. Nelly, in the same breath, 'we are greatly obliged to you for your history; and I am sure it deserves to be framed and glazed, and it ought to be hung up in the hall of every family, that all people may see the sad effects of pride, and how little cause people have, because they are rich, to despise those who are poor; since it frequently happens, that those who this year are like little kings, may the next be beggars; and then they will repent, when it is too late, of all their pride and unkindness they showed to those beneath them.'

Here the conversation was put a stop to by the bell ringing, and John being ordered to drive to the door. I, who during the whole of the history had been feasting upon a mince-pie, now thought it safer to conceal myself in a little hole in the wainscot of the closet, where, finding myself very safe, I did not awake till midnight. After the family were all retired to rest, I peeped out of the hole, and there saw just such another frightful trap as that which was the prelude to poor Softdown's sufferings. Startled at the sight, I retreated back as expeditiously as possible, nor ever stopped till I found my way into a bed-chamber, where lay two little girls fast asleep.

I looked about for some time, peeping into every hole and corner before I could find any thing to eat, there being not so much as a candle in the room with them. At last I crept into a little leathern trunk, which stood on a table, not shut down quite close: here I instantly smelt something good: but was obliged to gnaw through a great deal of linen to get at it; it was wrapped up in a lap-bag, amongst a vast quantity of work. However, I made my way through half a hundred folds, and at last was amply repaid, by finding out a nice piece of plum-cake, and the pips of an apple, which I could easily get at, one half of it having been eat away. Whilst I was thus engaged I heard a cat mew, and not knowing how near she might be, I endeavoured to jump out; but in the hurry I somehow or other entangled myself in the muslin, and pulled that, trunk and all, down with me; for the trunk stood half off the table, so that the least touch in the world overset it, otherwise my weight could never have tumbled it down.

The noise of the fall, however, waked the children, and I heard one say to the other, - 'Bless me! Mary, what is that noise? - What can it be? I am almost frightened out of my wits; do, pray, sister, hug me close!' 'Pooh!' replied the other, 'never mind it! What in the world need you be frightened at? What do you suppose will hurt you? It sounded as if something fell down; but as it has not fallen upon us, and I do not hear anybody stirring, or speaking as if they were hurt, what need we care about it? So pray, Nancy, let us go to sleep again; for as yet I have not had half sufficient, I am sure; I hope morning is not coming yet, for I am not at all ready to get up.' 'I am sure,' answered the other, 'I wish it was morning, and daylight now, for I should like to get up vastly, I do not like to lay here in the dark any longer; I have a great mind to ring the bell, and then mamma or somebody will come to us with a candle.'

'And what in the world,' rejoined Mary, 'will be the use of that? Do you want a candle to light you to look for the wounds the noise has given you; or what can you wish to disturb my mamma for? Come, let me cuddle you, and do go to sleep, child, for I cannot think what occasion there is for us to keep awake because we heard a noise; I never knew that noise had teeth or claws to hurt one with; and I am sure this has not hurt me; and so, whether you choose to lie awake or not, I will go to sleep, and so good-bye to you, and pray do not disturb me any more, for I cannot talk any longer.' 'But, Mary,' again replied the other, 'pray do not go to sleep yet, I want to speak to you.' 'Well, what do you want to say?' inquired Mary. 'Why, pray have you not very often,' said Nancy, 'heard of thieves breaking into people's houses and robbing them; and I am sadly afraid that noise was some rogues coming in; so pray, Mary, do not go to sleep, I am in such a fright and tremble you cannot think. Speak, Mary, have not you, I say, heard of thieves?' 'Yes,' replied Mary, in a very sleepy voice, 'a great many times.' 'Well, then, pray sister, do not go to sleep,' said Nancy, in a peevish accent, 'suppose, I say that noise I heard should be thieves, what should we do? What will become of us? O! what shall we do?' - 'Why, go to sleep, I tell you,' said Mary, 'as fast as you can; at least, do pray let me, for I cannot say I am in the smallest fear about house-breakers or house-makers either; and of all the robberies I ever heard of in all my life, I never heard of thieves stealing little girls; so do, there's a dear girl, go to sleep again, and do not so foolishly frighten yourself out of your wits for nothing.' 'Well,' replied Nancy, 'I will not keep you awake any longer; but I am sure I shall not be able to get another wink of sleep all night.'

Here the conversation ended, and I could not help

thinking how foolish it was for people to permit themselves to be terrified for nothing. Here is a little girl, now, thought I, in a nice clean room, and covered up warm in bed, with pretty green curtains drawn round her, to keep the wind from her head, and the light in the morning from her eyes; and yet she is distressing herself, and making herself really uncomfortable, and unhappy, only because I, a poor, little, harmless mouse, with scarcely strength sufficient to gnaw a nutshell, happened to jump from the table, and throw down, perhaps, her own box. - Oh! what a pity it is that people should so destroy their own comfort! How sweetly might this child have passed the night, if she had but, like her sister, wisely reflected that a noise could not possibly hurt them; and that, had any of the family occasioned it, by falling down, or running against anything in the dark which hurt them, most likely they would have heard some more stirring about.

And upon this subject the author cannot help, in human form (as well as in that of a mouse), observing how extremely ridiculous it is for people to suffer themselves to be terrified upon every trifling occasion that happens; as if they had no more resolution than a mouse itself, which is liable to be destroyed every meal it makes. And, surely, nothing can be more absurd than for children to be afraid of thieves and house-breakers; since, as little Mary said, they never want to seek after children. Money is all they want; and as children have very seldom much of that in their possession, they may assure themselves they are perfectly safe, and have therefore no occasion to alarm themselves if they hear a noise, without being able to make out what it is; unless, indeed, like the child I have just been writing about, they would be so silly as to be frightened at a little mouse; for most commonly the noises we hear, if we lay awake in the night, are caused by mice running about and playing behind the wainscot: and what reasonable person would suffer themselves to be alarmed by such little creatures as those? But it is time I should return to the history of my little make-believe companion, who went on, saying -

The conversation I have been relating I overheard as I lay concealed in a shoe that stood close by the bedside, and into which I ran the moment I jumped off the table, and where I kept snug till the next morning; when, just as the clock was striking eight, the same Mrs. Nelly, whom I saw the day before in the kitchen, entered the apartment, and accosted the young ladies, saying, 'Good morning to you, ladies, do you know that it is time to get up?' 'Then, pray, Nelly, lace my stays, will you?' said Miss Nancy. 'But lace mine first, and give me my other shoes; for those I wore yesterday must be brushed, because I stepped in the dirt, and so when you go down you must remember, and take and brush them, and then let me have them again,' said Mary; 'but come and dress me now.'

Well, thought I, this is a rude way of speaking, indeed, something like Miss Nancy Artless, at the house where my poor dear Softdown was so cruelly massacred; I am sure I hope I shall not meet with the like fate here, and I wish I was safe out of this shoe; for, perhaps, presently it will be wanted to be put on Mary's foot; and I am sure I must not expect to meet any mercy from a child who shows so bad a disposition as to speak to a servant in so uncivil a manner, for no good-natured person would do that.

With these kind of reflections I was amusing myself for some little time, when, all on a sudden, they were put an end to, by my finding the shoe in which I was concealed, hastily taken up; and before I had time to recollect what I had best do, I was almost killed by some violent blows I received, which well nigh broke every bone in my skin. I crept quite up to the toe of the shoe, so that I was not at all seen, and the maid, when she took up the shoes, held one in one hand, and the other in the other, by their heels, and then slapped them hard together, to beat out of some of the dust which was in them. This she repeated three or four times, till I was quite stunned; and how or which way I tumbled or got out, I know not; but when I came to myself, I was close up behind the foot of a table, in a large apartment, where were several children, and a gentleman and a lady, all conversing together with the greatest good humour and harmony.

The first words I heard distinctly enough to remember, were those of a little boy, about five years old, who, with eagerness exclaimed - 'I forget you! no that I never shall. If I was to go a hundred thousand miles off, I am sure I shall never forget you. What! do you think I should ever, as long as I live, if it is a million of years, forget my own dear papa and mamma? No; that I should not, I am very, very sure I never should.' 'Well, but Tom,' interrupted the gentleman, 'if in a million of years you should not forget us, I dare say, in less than two months you will forget our advice, and before you have been at school half that time, you will get to squabbling with and tricking the other boys, just as they do with one another; and instead of playing at all times with the strictest openness and honour, you will, I sadly fear, learn to cheat, and deceive, and pay no attention to what your mother and I have been telling you.' 'No', that I am sure I sha'n't!' replied the boy. 'What! do you think I shall be so wicked as to turn a thief, and cheat people?' 'I dare say, my dear,' resumed the father, 'you will not do what we call thieving; but as I know there are many naughty boys in all schools, I am afraid they will teach you to commit dishonourable actions, and to tell you there is no harm in them, and that they are signs of cleverness and spirit, and qualifications very necessary for every boy to possess.' 'Aye, that's sure enough,' said the boy, who appeared about ten years old, 'for they almost all declare, that if a boy is not sharp and cunning, he might almost as well be out of the world as in it. But, as you say, papa, I hate such behaviour, I am sure there is one of our boys, who is so wonderfully clever and acute, as they call him, that I detest ever having any thing to do with him; for unless one watches him as a cat would watch a mouse, he is sure to cheat or play one some trick or other.' 'What sort of tricks do you mean?' inquired the little boy. 'Why, I will tell you,' replied the other. 'You know nothing of the games we have at school, so if I was to tell you how he plays at them, you would not understand what I meant. But you know what walking about blindfold is, don't you? Well! one day, about a dozen boys agreed to have a blind race, and the boy who got nearest the goal, which was a stick driven in the ground with a shilling upon the top of it, was to win the shilling, provided he did it fairly without seeing.' 'I suppose,' interrupted Tom, 'you mean the boy who got to the stick first.' 'No, I do not,' replied his brother, 'I mean what I say, the boy who got nearest it, no matter whether he came first or last; the fun was to see them try to keep in a straight path, with their eyes tied up, whilst they wander quite in the wrong, and not to try who could run fastest. Well! when they, were all blinded, and twisted round three or four times before they were suffered to set off, they directed their steps the way they thought would directly conduct them to the goal; and some of them had almost reached it, when Sharply (the boy I mentioned) who had placed a shilling upon the stick, for they drew lots who should do that, and he who furnished the money was to stand by it, to observe who won it by coming nearest; well, Sharply, I say, just as they came close to it, moved away softly to another place, above three yards distant from any of them (for I should have told you, that if none of them got within three yards, the shilling was to remain his, and they were each to give him a penny.) So then he untied their eyes, and insisted upon it they had all of them lost. But two or three of us happened to be by, and so we said he had cheated them, and ought not to keep the money, as it had fairly been won by Smyth. But he would not give it up, so it made a quarrel between him and Smyth, and at last they fought, and Mr. Chiron confined them both in the school all the rest of the afternoon, and when he heard what the quarrel was about, he took the shilling from Sharply, and called him a mean-spirited cheat; but he would not let Smyth have it, because he said he deserved to lose it for fighting about such a trifle, and so it was put into the forfeit-money.'

'But pray do not you think Sharply behaved extremely wrong?' 'Shamefully so, indeed,' said the gentleman. 'I never could have any opinion of a boy 'who could act so dishonourably,' said the lady, 'let his cleverness be what it would.' 'Pray, Frank, tell me some more,' said the little boy. 'More!' replied Frank, 'I could tell you an hundred such kind of things. One time, as Peter Light was walking up the yard, with some damsons in his hat, Sharply ran by, and as he passed, knocked his hat out of his hand, for the sake of scrambling for as many as he could get himself. And sometimes, after the pie-woman has been there, he gets such heaps of tarts you cannot think, by his different tricks: perhaps he will buy a currant tart himself; then he would go about, calling out, "Who'll change a cheesecake for a currant tart?" and now-and-then he will add, "and half a bun into the bargain!" Then two or three of the boys call out, "I will, I will!" and when they go to hold out their cheesecakes to him, he snatches them out of their hands before they are aware, and runs away in an instant; and whilst they stand for a moment in astonishment, he gets so much ahead of them that he eats them up before they can again overtake him. At other times, when he sees a boy beginning to eat his cake, he will come and talk carelessly to him for a few moments, and then all of a sudden call out, "Look! look! look!-there!" pointing his finger as if to show him something wonderful; and when the other, without suspecting any mischief, turns his head to see what has so surprised him, away he snatches the cake, and runs off with it, cramming it into his mouth in a moment.

'And when he plays at Handy-dandy, Jack-a-dandy, which will you have, upper hand or lower? if you happen to guess right, he slips whatever you are playing with into his other hand; and that you know is not playing fair; and so many of the boys tell him; but he does not mind any of us. And as he is clever at his learning, and always does his exercise quite right, Mr. Chiron (who indeed does not know of his tricks) is very fond of him, and is for ever saying what a clever fellow he is, and proposing him as an example to the rest of the boys; and I do believe many of them imitate his deceitful, cheating tricks, only for the sake of being thought like him.'

'Aye! it is a sad thing,' interrupted the gentleman, 'that people who are blessed with sense and abilities to behave well, should so misuse them as to set a bad, instead of a good example to others, and by that means draw many into sin, who otherwise, perhaps, might never have acted wrong. Was this Sharply, you have been speaking of, a dunce and blockhead at his book, he would never gain the commendations that Mr. Chiron now bestows upon him; and, consequently, no boy would wish to be thought like him; his bad example, therefore, would not be of half the importance it now is.

'Only think, then, my dear children, how extremely wicked it is, for those who are blessed with understandings capable of acting as they should do, and making people admire them, at the same time to be guilty of such real and great sin. For, however children at play may like to trick and deceive each other, and call it only play or fun, still, let me tell you, they are much mistaken if they flatter themselves there is no harm in it. It is a very wrong way of behaviour; it is mean, it is dishonorable, and it is wicked; and the boy or girl who would ever permit themselves to act in so unjustifiable a manner, however they may excel in their learning, or exterior accomplishments, can never be deserving of esteem, confidence, or regard. What esteem or respect could I ever entertain of a person's sense or learning, who made no better use of it than to practise wickedness with more dexterity and grace than he otherwise would be enabled to do? Or, what confidence could I ever place in the person who, I knew, only wanted a convenient opportunity to defraud, trick, and deceive me? Or, what regard and love could I possibly entertain for such a one, who, unless I kept a constant watch over, as I must over a wild beast, would, like a wild beast, be sure to do me some injury? Would it be possible, I say, to love such a character, whatever shining abilities or depth of learning he might possess? Ask your own hearts, my dears, whether you think you could?'

To this they all answered at once, 'No, that I could not,' and 'I am sure I could not.' 'Well, then,' resumed the father, 'only think how odious that conduct must be, which robs us of the esteem, confidence, and love of our fellow-creatures; and that too, notwithstanding we may at the same time be very clever, and have a great deal of sense and learning. But, for my part, I confess I know not the least advantage of our understanding or our learning, unless we make a proper use of them. Knowing a great deal, and having read a great many books, will be of no service to us, unless we are careful to make a proper use of that knowledge, and to improve by what we read, otherwise the time we so bestow is but lost, and we might as well spend the whole of our lives in idleness.

'Always remember, therefore, my loves, that the whole end of our taking the trouble to instruct you, or putting ourselves to the expense of sending you to school, or your attending to what is taught you, is, that you may grow better men and women than you otherwise would be; and unless, therefore, you do improve, we might as well spare ourselves the pains and expense, and you need not take the trouble of learning; since, if you will act wickedly, all our labour is but thrown away to no manner of purpose.

'Mr. and Mrs. Sharply, how I pity them! What sorrow must they endure, to behold their son acting in the manner you have described; for nothing can give so much concern to a fond parent's heart, as to see their children, for whom they have taken so much pains, turn out naughty; and to deceive and cheat! What can be worse than that? I hope, my dear children, you will never, any of you, give us that dreadful misery! I hope, my dear Tom, I hope you will never learn any of those detestable ways your brother has been telling you of. And if it was not that you will often be obliged to see such things when you mix with other children, I should be sorry you should even hear of such bad actions, as I could wish you to pass through life without so much as knowing such wickedness ever existed; hut that is impossible. There are so many naughty people in the world, that you will often be obliged to see and hear of crimes which I hope you will shudder to think of committing yourselves; and being warned of them beforehand, I hope it will put you more upon your guard, not to be tempted, upon any consideration, to give the least encouragement to them, much less to practise them yourselves.

'Perhaps, Tom, if your brother had not, by telling us of Sharply's tricks, given me an opportunity of warning you how extremely wrong and wicked they are, you might when you were at school, have thought them very clever, and marks of genius; and therefore, like others of the boys, have tried to imitate them, and by that means have become as wicked, mean, and dishonourable yourself. And only think how it would have grieved your mamma and me, to find the next holidays, our dear little Tom, instead of being that honest, open, generous-hearted boy he now is, changed into a deceiver, a cheat, a liar, one whom we could place no trust or confidence in; for, depend upon it, the person who will, when at play, behave unfair, would not scruple to do so in even other action of his life.

Dorothy Kilner

And the boy who will deceive for the sake of a marble, or the girl who would act ungenerously, for the sake of a doll's cap or a pin, will, when grown up, be ready to cheat and over-reach in their trades, or any affairs they may have to transact. And you may assure yourselves that numbers of people who are every year hanged, began at first to be wicked by practising those little dishonourable mean actions, which so many children are too apt to do at play, without thinking of their evil consequences.

'I think, my dear,' said he, turning to his wife, 'I have heard you mention a person who you were acquainted with when a girl, who at last was hanged for stealing, I think, was not she?' 'No,' replied the lady, 'she was not hanged, she was transported for one-and-twenty years.' 'Pray, madam, how transported? what is that?' inquired one of the children. 'People, my dear,' resumed the lady, 'are transported when they have committed crimes, which, according to the laws of our land, are not thought quite wicked enough to be hanged for; but still too bad to suffer them to continue amongst other people. So, instead of hanging them, the judge orders that they shall be sent on board a ship, built on purpose to hold naughty people, and carried away from all their friends, a great many miles distant, commonly to America, where they are sold as slaves, to work very hard for as many years as they are transported for. And the person your papa mentioned was sold for twenty-one years; but she died before that time was out, as most of them do: they are generally used very cruelly, and work very hard; and besides, the heat of the climate seldom agrees with anybody who has been used to live in England, and so they generally die before their time is expired, and never have an opportunity of seeing their friends any more, after they are once sent away. How should any of you, my dears, like to be sent away from your papa and me, and your brothers and sisters, and uncles and aunts, and all your friends, and never) never see us any more; and only keep company with naughty, cross, wicked people, and labour very hard, and suffer a great deal of sickness, and such a number of different hardships, you cannot imagine? Only think how shocking it must be! How should you like it?' 'Oh', not at all, not at all,' was echoed from everyone in the room.

'But such,' rejoined their mother, 'is the punishment naughty people have; and such was the punishment the person your papa spoke of had; who, when she was young, no more expected to come to such an end than any of you do. I was very well acquainted with her, and often used to play with her, and she (like the boy Frank has been talking of) used to think it a mark of cleverness to be able to deceive; and for the sake of winning the game she was engaged in, would not scruple committing any little unfair action, which would give her the advantage.

'I remember one time, at such a trifling game as pushpin, she gave me a very bad opinion of her; for I observed, instead of pushing the pin as she ought to do, she would try to lift it up with her finger a little, to make it cross over the other.

'And when we were all at cards, she would peep, to find out the pictured ones, that she might have them in her own hand.

'And when we played at any game which had forfeits, she would try, by different little artifices, to steal back her own before the time of crying them came; or, if she was the person who was to cry them, as you call it, she would endeavour to see whose came next, that she might order the penalty accordingly.

'Or if we were playing at hide and seek, she would put what we had to hide either in her own pocket, or throw it into the fire, so that it would be impossible to find it; and then, after making her companions hunt for it for an hour, till their patience was quite tired, and they gave out; she would burst out in a loud laugh! and say she only did it for fun. But, for my part, I never could see any joke in such kind of things: the meanness, the baseness, the dish on our, which attended it always, in my opinion, took off all degree of cleverness, or pleasure from such actions.

'There was another of her sly tricks which I forgot to mention, and that was, if at tea, or any other time, she got first to the plate of cake or bread, she would place the piece she liked best where she thought it would come to her turn to have it: or if at breakfast she saw her sisters' basin have the under crust in it, and they happened not to be by, or to see her, she would take it out, and put her own, which she happened not to like so well, in the stead.

'Only think, my dears, what frightful, sly, naughty tricks to be guilty of! And from practising these, which she said there was no harm in, and she only did them in play, and for a bit of fun, at last she came, by degrees, to be guilty of greater. She two or three different times, when she was not seen, stole things out of shops; and one day, when she was upon a visit, and thought she could do it cleverly, without being discovered, put a couple of table spoons into her pocket. The footman who was waiting happened to see her; but fearing to give offence, he took no notice of it till after she was gone home, when he told his master, who, justly provoked at being so ill-treated, by a person to whom he had shown every civility, went after her, called in her own two maids, and his footman, as witnesses, and then insisted upon examining her pockets, where he indeed found his own two spoons. He then sent for proper officers to secure her, had her taken into custody, and for that offence it was that she was transported.

'Thus, my dear children, you see the shocking consequence of ever suffering such vile habits to grow upon us; and I hope the example of this unhappy woman (which I assure you is a true story) will be sufficient to warn you for ever, for a single time, being guilty of so detestable a crime, lest you should, like her, by degrees come to experience her fatal punishment.'

Just as the lady said these words a bell rang, and all getting up together, they went out of the room, the young one calling out, 'To dinner! to dinner! to dinner! here we all go to dinner!'

And I will seek for one too, said I to myself, (creeping out as soon as I found I was alone) for I feel very faint and hungry. I looked and looked about a long while, for I could move but slow, on account of the bruises I had received in the shoe. At last under the table, round which the family had been sitting, I found a pincushion, which, being stuffed with bran, afforded me enough to satisfy my hunger, but was excessively dry and unsavoury; yet, bad as it was, I was obliged to be content at that time with it; and had nearly done eating when the door opened, and in ran two or three of the children. Frightened out of my senses almost, I had just time to escape down a little hole in the floor, made by one of the knots in the wood slipping out, and there I heard one of the girls exclaim -

'O dear! who now has cut my pincushion? it was you did it, Tom.' 'No, indeed I did not,' replied he. 'Then it was you, Mary.' 'No, I know nothing of it,' answered she. 'Then it was you, Hetty.' 'That I am sure it was not,' said she; 'I am sure, I am certain it was not me; I am positive it was not.' 'Ah,' replied the other, 'I dare say it was.' 'Yes, I think it is most likely,' said Mary. 'And so do I too,' said Tom. 'And pray why do you all think so?' inquired Hetty, in an angry tone. 'Because,' said the owner of the pincushion, 'you are the only one who ever tells fibs; you told a story, you know, about the fruit; you told a story too about the currant jelly; and about putting your fingers in the butter, at breakfast; and therefore there is a very great reason why we should suspect you more than anybody else.' 'But I am sure,' said she, bursting into tears, 'I am very sure I have not meddled with it.' 'I do not at all know that,' replied the other, 'and I do think it was you; for I am certain if any one else had done it they would not deny it; and it could not come into this condition by itself, somebody must have done it; and I dare say it was you; so say no more about it.'

Here the dispute was interrupted by somebody calling them out of the room; and I could not help making some reflections on what had passed. How dreadful a crime, thought I, is lying and falsity; to what sad mortifications does it subject the person who is ever wicked enough to commit it; and how does it expose them to the contempt of everyone, and make them to be suspected of faults they are even perfectly free from. Little Hetty now is innocent, with respect to the pincushion with which her sister charges her, as any of the others; yet, because she has before forfeited her honour, she can gain no credit: no one believes what she says, she is thought to be guilty of the double fault of spoiling the pincushion, and what is still worse, of lying to conceal it; whilst the other children are at once believed, and their words depended upon.

Surely, surely, thought I, if people would but reflect upon the contempt, the shame, and the difficulties which lies expose them to, they would never be guilty of so terrible a vice, which subjects them to the scorn of all they converse with, and renders them at all times suspected, even though they should, as in the case of Hetty, really speak the truth. Such were my reflections upon falsehood, nor could I help altogether blaming the owner of the pincushion for her hasty judgment relating to it. Somebody, she was certain, must have done it; it was impossible it could come so by itself. That, to be sure, was very true; but then she never recollected that it was possible a little mouse might put it in that condition. Ah! thought I to myself, what pity is it, that human creatures, who are blest with understanding and faculties so superior to any species, should not make better use of them; and learn, from daily experience, to grow wiser and better for the future. This one instance of the pincushion, may teach (and surely people engaged in life must hourly find more) how dangerous it is to draw hasty conclusions, and to condemn people upon suspicion, as also the many, great, and bad consequences of lying.

Scarcely had I finished these soliloquies when a great knock at the house door made me give such a start that I fell off the joist on which I was standing, and then ran straight forwards till I came out at a little hole I found in the bricks above the parlour window: from that I descended into the road, and went on unmolested till I reached a malt-house, about whose various apartments, never staying long in the same, I continued to live; till one night, all on a sudden, I was alarmed by fire, which obliged me to retreat with the greatest expedition.

I passed numberless rats and mice in my way, who, like myself, were driven forth by the flames; but, alas! among them I found not my brother. Despairing, therefore, of ever seeing him again, I determined, if possible, to find my way back to you, who before had shown me such kindness. Numberless were the fatigues and difficulties I had to encounter in my journey here; one while in danger from hungry cats, at another almost perished with cold and want of food.

But it is needless to enumerate every particular; I should but tire your patience was I to attempt it; so I will hasten to a conclusion of my history, only telling you how you came to find me in that melancholy condition from which your mercy has now raised me.

I came into your house one evening concealed in the middle of a floor-cloth, which the maid had rolled up and set at the outside of the back door, whilst she swept the passage, and neglected to take it in again till the evening, In that I hid myself, and upon her laying it down, ran with all speed down the cellar-stairs, where I continued till the family were all gone to bed. Then I returned back, and came into your closet, where the scent of some figs tempted me to get into the jar in which you found me. I concealed myself among them, and after feasting most deliciously, fell asleep, from which I was awakened by hearing a voice say, "Who has left the cover off the fig-jar?" and at the same time I was involved in darkness by having it put on. In vain I endeavoured to remove it, the figs were so low, that when I stood on them I could but just touch it with my lips, and the jar being stone I could not possibly fasten my nails to hang by the side.

In this dismal situation therefore I was constrained to stay, my apprehensions each day increasing as my food diminished, till at last, after feeding very sparingly for some days, it was quite exhausted; and I had endured the inexpressible tortures of hunger for three days and three nights, when you happily released me, and by your compassion restored me once more to life and liberty. Condescend, therefore, to preserve that life you have so lengthened, and take me under your protection.

'That most gladly,' interrupted I, 'I will do: you will live in this large green-flowered tin canister, and run in and out when you please, and I will keep you constantly supplied with food. But I must now shut you in, for the cat has this moment entered the room.'

And now I cannot take leave of all my little readers, without once more begging them, for their own sakes, to endeavour to follow all the good advice the mouse has been giving them; and likewise warning them to shun all those vices and follies, the practice of which renders children so contemptible and wicked.

Notes

Notes

Notes

Notes

Notes

Notes

Choose from Thousands of 1stWorldLibrary Classics By

Ada Leverson
Adolphus William Ward
Aesop
Agatha Christie
Alexander Aaronsohn
Alexander Kielland
Alexandre Dumas
Alfred Gatty
Alfred Ollivant
Alice Duer Miller
Alice Turner Curtis
Alice Dunbar
Ambrose Bierce
Amelia E. Barr
Andrew Lang
Andrew McFarland Davis
Andy Adams
Anna Sewell
Annie Besant
Annie Hamilton Donnell
Annie Payson Call
Annonaymous
Anton Chekhov
Arnold Bennett
Arthur Conan Doyle
Arthur M. Winfield
Arthur Ransome
Atticus
B.H. Baden-Powell
B. M. Bower
Baroness Emmuska Orczy
Baroness Orczy
Basil King
Bayard Taylor
Ben Macomber
Bertha Muzzy Bower
Bjornstjerne Bjornson
Booth Tarkington
Boyd Cable
Bram Stoker
C. Collodi
C. E. Orr
C. M. Ingleby
Carolyn Wells
Catherine Parr Traill
Charles A. Eastman
Charles Dickens
Charles Dudley Warner
Charles Farrar Browne

Charles Ives
Charles Kingsley
Charles Klein
Charles Lathrop Pack
Charles Whibley
Charles Willing Beale
Charlotte M. Braeme
Charlotte M. Yonge
Charlotte Perkins Stetson
Clair W. Hayes
Clarence Day Jr.
Clarence E. Mulford
Clemence Housman
Confucius
Cornelis DeWitt Wilcox
Cyril Burleigh
D. H. Lawrence
Daniel Defoe
David Garnett
Don Carlos Janes
Donald Keyhoe
Dorothy Kilner
Dougan Clark
Douglas Fairbanks
E. Nesbit
E.P.Roe
E. Phillips Oppenheim
Edgar Rice Burroughs
Edith Van Dyne
Edith Wharton
Edward J. O'Biren
Edward S. Ellis
Edwin L. Arnold
Eleanor Atkins
Eliot Gregory
Elizabeth Gaskell
Elizabeth McCracken
Elizabeth Von Arnim
Ellem Key
Emerson Hough
Emily Dickinson
Enid Bagnold
Enilor Macartney Lane
Erasmus W. Jones
Ernie Howard Pie
Ethel Turner
Ethel Watts Mumford
Eugenie Foa
Eugene Wood

Evelyn Everett-green
Everard Cotes
F. H. Cheley
F. J. Cross
Federick Austin Ogg
Ferdinand Ossendowski
Francis Bacon
Francis Darwin
Frances Hodgson Burnett
Frances Parkinson Keyes
Frank Gee Patchin
Frank Harris
Frank Jewett Mather
Frank L. Packard
Frank V. Webster
Frederic Stewart Isham
Frederick Trevor Hill
Frederick Winslow Taylor
Friedrich Kerst
Friedrich Nietzsche
Fyodor Dostoyevsky
G.A. Henty
G.K. Chesterton
Gabrielle E. Jackson
Garrett P. Serviss
Gaston Leroux
George Ade
Geroge Bernard Shaw
George Durston
George Ebers
George Eliot
George MacDonald
George Meredith
George Orwell
George Tucker
George W. Cable
George Wharton James
Gertrude Atherton
Grace E. King
Grace Gallatin
Grant Allen
Guillermo A. Sherwell
Gulielma Zollinger
Gustav Flaubert
H. A. Cody
H. B. Irving
H.C. Bailey
H. G. Wells
H. H. Munro

H. Irving Hancock
H. Rider Haggard
H. W. C. Davis
Hamilton Wright Mabie
Hans Christian Andersen
Harold Avery
Harold McGrath
Harriet Beecher Stowe
Harry Houidini
Helent Hunt Jackson
Helen Nicolay
Hendrik Conscience
Hendy David Thoreau
Henri Barbusse
Henrik Ibsen
Henry Adams
Henry Ford
Henry Frost
Henry James
Henry Jones Ford
Henry Seton Merriman
Henry W Longfellow
Herbert A. Giles
Herbert N. Casson
Herman Hesse
Homer
Honore De Balzac
Horace Walpole
Horatio Alger Jr.
Howard Pyle
Howard R. Garis
Hugh Lofting
Hugh Walpole
Humphry Ward
Ian Maclaren
Inez Haynes Gillmore
Irving Bacheller
Israel Abrahams
Ivan Turgenev
J.G.Austin
J. Henri Fabre
J. M. Barrie
J. Macdonald Oxley
J. S. Fletcher
J. S. Knowles
J. Storer Clouston
Jack London
Jacob Abbott
James Allen
James Andrews
James Baldwin

James DeMille
James Joyce
James Lane Allen
James Lane Allen
James Oliver Curwood
James Oppenheim
James Otis
James R. Driscoll
Jane Austen
Jens Peter Jacobsen
Jerome K. Jerome
John Burroughs
John Cournos
John F. Kennedy
John Gay
John Glasworthy
John Habberton
John Joy Bell
John Kendrick Bangs
John Milton
John Philip Sousa
Jonas Lauritz Idemil Lie
Jonathan Swift
Joseph A. Altsheler
Joseph Carey
Joseph Conrad
Joseph E. Badger Jr
Joseph Hergesheimer
Joseph Jacobs
Julian Hawthrone
Julies Vernes
Justin Huntly McCarthy
Kakuzo Okakura
Kenneth Grahame
Kenneth McGaffey
Kate Langley Bosher
Kate Langley Bosher
Katherine Cecil Thurston
Katherine Stokes
L. A. Abbot
L. T. Meade
L. Frank Baum
Latta Griswold
Laura Lee Hope
Laurence Housman
Leo Tolstoy
Leonid Andreyev
Lewis Carroll
Lilian Bell
Lloyd Osbourne
Louis Tracy

Louisa May Alcott
Lucy Fitch Perkins
Lucy Maud Montgomery
Lydia Miller Middleton
Lyndon Orr
M. Corvus
M. H. Adams
Margaret E. Sangster
Margaret Vandercook
Margret Penrose
Maria Edgeworth
Maria Thompson Daviess
Mariano Azuela
Marion Polk Angellotti
Mark Overton
Mark Twain
Mary Austin
Mary Catherine Crowley
Mary Cole
Mary Hastings Bradley
Mary Roberts Rinehart
Mary Rowlandson
M. Wollstonecraft Shelley
Maud Lindsay
Max Beerbohm
Myra Kelly
Nathaniel Hawthrone
Nicolo Machiavelli
O. F. Walton
Oscar Wilde
Owen Johnson
P.G. Wodehouse
Paul and Mabel Thorne
Paul G. Tomlinson
Paul Severing
Percy Brebner
Peter B. Kyne
Plato
R. Derby Holmes
R. L. Stevenson
R. S. Ball
Rabindranath Tagore
Rahul Alvares
Ralph Henry Barbour
Ralph Waldo Emmerson
Rene Descartes
Rex Beach
Rex E. Beach
Richard Harding Davis
Richard Jefferies
Richard Le Gallienne

Robert Barr
Robert Frost
Robert Gordon Anderson
Robert L. Drake
Robert Lansing
Robert Lynd
Robert Michael Ballantyne
Robert W. Chambers
Rosa Nouchette Carey
Rudyard Kipling
Samuel B. Allison
Samuel Hopkins Adams
Sarah Bernhardt
Selma Lagerlof
Sherwood Anderson
Sigmund Freud
Standish O'Grady
Stanley Weyman
Stella Benson
Stephen Crane
Stewart Edward White
Stijn Streuvels
Swami Abhedananda

Swami Parmananda
T. S. Ackland
T. S. Arthur
The Princess Der Ling
Thomas A. Janvier
Thomas A Kempis
Thomas Anderton
Thomas Bailey Aldrich
Thomas Bulfinch
Thomas De Quincey
Thomas H. Huxley
Thomas Hardy
Thomas More
Thornton W. Burgess
U. S. Grant
Valentine Williams
Various Authors
Victor Appleton
Virginia Woolf
Walter Camp
Walter Scott
Washington Irving
Wilbur Lawton

Wilkie Collins
Willa Cather
Willard F. Baker
William Dean Howells
William le Queux
W. Makepeace Thackeray
William W. Walter
Winston Churchill
Yei Theodora Ozaki
Yogi Ramacharaka
Young E. Allison
Zane Grey

Lightning Source UK Ltd.
Milton Keynes UK
UKHW012259191021
392503UK00008B/364/J